"Tell us A

108 Further Stories
for Primary School
Worship Assemblies,

with Prayers, suggested Hymns,
and Teachers' Notes,
for Autumn, Spring,
and Summer Terms.

———————————

(This book may be used in conjunction
with the first volume, "Tell us a Story.")

Rev. Dr. George E. Stewart,
B.A., M.A.

Published by
Topical Resources

First Published April 1996

Published by:
Topical Resources

P.O. Box 329,
Broughton,
Preston,

Tel: 01772 863158,

PR3 5LT

ISBN 1 872977 23 5

Typeset and Printed by T. Snape & Co. Ltd., Boltons Court, Preston, Lancashire.
Tel: 01772 254553

Preface

"Tell Us a Another" is a second volume of stories written for the Worship Assembly of the Primary School. The required third re-printing of the first volume in a similar number of years, revealed the keen interest taken by Headteachers and Religious Experts in what happens in the Primary School Assembly. Both County schools, and Church schools of all the major denominations have found the "First" book useful.

The simple, fast moving style, and the language of the stories had been chosen deliberately. The stories are meant to be told, rather than read. The style of story telling has been adapted to suit the wide age range of Primary School pupils. The stories in this second volume, (as in the first volume), have been tested, in the actual Primary School Worship Assembly situation. Qualified Teachers have constructively criticised them, and the style and language has been amended where it was thought to be necessary.

The stories cover the three terms of a school year. Each week has a single theme, dealt with by two stories applicable to the children's life experience, and one story from the Bible. A short prayer is added after each story, based on the theme for the week. A hymn is suggested, taken from one of three popular Hymn Books used by Primary Schools.

A "Teachers' Note" has been added at the end of each story, which usually makes three valid points. The story as it unfolds, usually contains a moral, or a social problem, which is of interest to the children. They are meant to be involved in the moral decisions, as the Teacher tells the story.

I have been influenced in my writing by the answers which I received to a Questionnaire which I sent out to thirty Primary schools. The Headteachers' reply listed the difficulties of the Worship Assembly, as: (1) The Pupil's limited attention span. (2) The Pupils live in a television age, and consequently, pictures come easier to children than words. (3) Worship is not always pitched at the child's age level. (4) Religion is not relevant to the parental background. (5) Pupils, generally, no longer attend Sunday School.

Although the book is based on the progression of the school year, the stories may be used individually to suit events in the school, or in the pupil's life experience, eg. An accident, a local celebration, a birthday, Christian Aid Week, a farewell, holidays, or the recognised special days. The choice is left to the professionalism, integrity, and sensitivity of the Teacher.

The stories have been written under the provisions of the 1988 Education Reform Act, where a distinction has been drawn between the Worship Assembly, and Religious Education. The book has been written with, "a broadly Christian approach." It treats the stories objectively, without denominational bias. It leaves the matter of interpretation to the Teacher, and to the imagination of the children.

There are many stories here which could readily be used by Sunday school Teachers, or in Church Family Services.

Contents

Autumn Term

Spring Term

Summer Term

Hymn Book Abbreviations.

The suggested Hymns for these Worship Assemblies are to be found in one of three popular Hymn Books used by Schools.

(C. & P.1.) Come and Praise. Book 1.   B.B.C. Publications

(C. & P.2.) Come and Praise Book 2.   B.B.C. Publications

(J. P.) Junior Praise. (Combined Words Edition.)

Marshall Pickering

Autumn Term

2

(a) Return to a Fresh Start.

It was the school holidays. The Smith children lived in Birmingham. They were very pleased with themselves, because their family owned a caravan. Every Summer Dad would hitch the caravan to the family car and the three children, Roger, Sally, and Kevin would all squeeze into the back seat, not forgetting to wear their seat-belts! Mother sat in the front seat, while Dad, was the driver.

They were off to the seaside in Wales for two weeks holiday. The family owned a beautiful big grey Tom cat called, "Tiger". Sometimes the family would neglect the cat. However, they did not do this intentionally. Sometimes, they just forgot that Tiger was there.

Just as Dad was driving away, Roger shouted out, "What about Tiger? We have forgotten the cat! We cannot leave Tiger behind, Dad!" So Dad had to go down the garden, and look for Tiger. He lifted Tiger off the garden wall, and passed the cat to the children inside the car.

The children set the cat on the ledge, along the back window. Dad warned the children, that if the car stopped at the traffic lights, they were not to open the window, in case Tiger might jump out and escape. At last they were off to the seaside!

The Smith family had a lovely holiday in Wales. Most days were sunny, and the children spent the time enjoying themselves on the rocks, sand and in the sea. Each time they had a meal, they also put out a dish of cat food, or a saucer of milk for Tiger. Their beloved cat never went far away from their caravan.

When the holiday came to an end, the family packed their belongings into the caravan. They began the drive home again. Again, they allowed Tiger to sleep on the ledge near the back window of the car. When they reached Birmingham, the air in the car was rather warm. Kevin the youngest member of the family, forgot his father's warning. He opened the side window to get a breath of fresh air, just as the car stopped at the traffic lights. Before they could do anything, Tiger moved very quickly, and jumped out through the open window. In a moment he was gone from sight.

Mr. Smith stopped the car, and the family jumped out. They all helped to search the gardens alongside the road, but no-one could find Tiger. All they could do was to get into the car and drive home with very sad feelings. They all loved Tiger! There was no doubt about it, they had really lost their cat. Sally most of all missed Tiger. She cried every night when she was in bed.

Three weeks passed by. The school holidays were over, and the children went back to school again. On the third day, at play time in the school yard, Sally was with her school friends, when she saw a big thin grey cat walking very slowly, as if it were very tired. She thought to herself, "I must run into the cloakroom and bring a sandwich from my bag. I'll share it with this hungry-looking cat."

When Sally brought the sandwich, to her amazement, the big thin grey cat jumped up on to her shoulder and began to mew. Sally was a little bit frightened of the strange cat. Then all at once she realised that the cat was her own Tiger. He had been trying to find his way home for three long weeks. No wonder he looked so thin! Three weeks without a proper meal is a long time.

Sally brought Tiger into the class room. Her Teacher allowed Tiger to remain until school was over. The Teacher said that Tiger had come back to school after the Summer holidays just like the children! The children laughed at that. The Teacher taught the children about being kind to animals. In the art lesson, the children painted a picture of a cat. After school, Sally cuddled Tiger all the way home. Roger and Kevin were delighted to see Tiger, and they made him a special saucer of warm milk.

The family were delighted to see Tiger again, but deep inside they felt a little ashamed of themselves for not looking after the cat more carefully in the first place. They all made a promise to themselves, that they would make a fresh start. At home, as they sat around the meal table, they made a family resolution. They agreed that in future, they would take more care of their cat.

Maybe cats are a little like pigeons, which have a "homing instinct." Three weeks is a long time to have to walk through the streets of Birmingham, but the cat came home, that is the important thing. Schools are a kind of a home from home. Someone has said that where the heart lies, the feet will wander. Coming back to school, we also, can make a fresh start. We, too, can try harder than ever before!

Prayer:

> Heavenly Father, we thank you for our world.
> We thank you for insects, reptiles, animals, and fish.
> May we learn about animals in the wild.
> Help us to value farm animals.
> May we never be cruel to animals.
> Grant that like the family in the story,
> each one of us will make a fresh start
> and be good learners in school.   Amen.

Hymn:

> Have you seen the pussy cat? (J.P. 72)

Teachers' Note: (1) Pets need proper care. (2) The family had neglected the cat by nearly leaving it behind, and by allowing it to jump out of the car. (3) Many animals have a "homing instinct". Children also love to return home and to return to school. The Bible uses animals to teach lessons to human beings. (The story of the lost sheep in St. Luke 15.).

(b) Return of the Letter   *Week 1   Returning*

Laura's Auntie bought her a new tooth-brush. It was a bright red colour, with stiff white bristles. Laura read the back of the packet, and she discovered that she could enter a competition. There were two parts to the competition. First, she had to write a clever sentence about cleaning one's teeth. Secondly, she had to answer the question, "How many teeth do you have in your mouth, if they are all there?"

The rules also were laid down. When a competitor filled in the answers, two envelopes had to be used. One envelope had to be addressed to the competition office. A second envelope, addressed to herself, had also to be included, inside the first envelope. A stamp had to be stuck on the right hand corner of each envelope. Laura, prepared the two envelopes. Her Dad gave to her two stamps from his wallet.

Next, Laura set to trying to make up a sentence about cleaning one's teeth. She thought of many good sentences, but they never seemed to be just right. At last, she wrote, "Your teeth are precious, clean them after meals."

Laura went to the mirror, and she opened her mouth very wide. She counted her upper teeth, and found that she had sixteen teeth. She then counted her lower teeth, and found that she had another sixteen teeth. Laura wrote down the two numbers 16 and 16. She added them up very quickly, and found that she had thirty-two teeth in her mouth. She again read the question in the competition, "How many teeth do you have in your mouth, if they are all there? She wrote "Thirty-two teeth." Laura quickly put the written answers with the addressed envelope, inside one of the envelopes. She ran down to the Post Box, and posted it.

Laura used to wonder in class at school, whether she had won the competition or not. After three months, she forgot all about the matter. However, she never forgot to clean her teeth. She did not just clean them by rubbing the brush across her mouth. Laura knew that she must also brush her teeth, up and down, so as to clean between them.

One day after school, she came home and found that the postman had delivered a letter addressed to her. She examined the hand-writing. Laura realised that the envelope was written by herself. It was news of the competition. The letter had returned!

With trembling hands, and a heart pounding with excitement, she opened the envelope. There she read, "Dear Laura, You are one of the five hundred people.

who have won a prize. Thank you for your clever answers! The prize will follow later in the month."

Sure enough, one Saturday morning, the postman came again. He knocked on the front door. He was carrying a packet, which could not be pushed through the letter-box. He handed Laura the packet. Inside the packet were ten large tubes of tooth paste, ten new tooth brushes, and a lovely silver watch. On Monday morning at school, Laura gave the ten tooth-brushes, and the ten tubes of tooth paste to her best friends at school. She wanted them to share her good fortune. She kept the silver watch for herself. Laura rightly felt that she deserved to keep it.

Prayer:

> Lord, you have given us wonderful bodies.
> Help us to keep our bodies healthy and clean.
> We have teeth, and we have appetites,
> and we have food to eat.
> Bless those children around the world,
> who also have teeth, but may have little food.   Amen.

Hymn:

> He gave me eyes so I could see. (C&P. 1. 18)

Teachers' Note: (1) Something always comes back in return for any hard work that we may do. (This does not mean that we will always win a prize). (2) Laura was not a selfish girl, she shared her prize with other children. (3) Cleanliness comes next to godliness. For health reasons we ought to clean our teeth.

(c) **Return of the Dove**   *Week 1   Returning*

Did you know that most of the ancient religions tell a story about a "Flood"? The Bible story is perhaps the best known. Because the earth was full of violence, God was very angry with human beings. God told Noah who was the only righteous man, that he was going to destroy the wicked people. He instructed Noah to build a great ship of Gopher wood. The ship was known as the "ark". It was to have three decks, with stalls, and a door in the side of the top deck.

The wood inside and outside the ark was to be covered with pitch (tar) to keep out the water. God then told Noah to bring a male and a female of every kind of animal, bird, and reptile into the ark. Noah was also told to store enough food for the animals and his family in the huge boat. Noah did everything exactly as God had told him.

Noah was six hundred years old, when the flood began. He had brought into the ark, his wife, and his three sons, Shem, Ham, and Japeth, and their wives. Then, the heavy rain poured down for forty days and nights. All the living people and animals were drowned in the flood which covered even the mountains.

The wind began to blow, and the water gradually began to go down, until after one hundred and fifty days, the ark came to rest on Mount Ararat. Three months passed, and other hill-tops began to appear above the water.

Noah opened a window in the ark, and released a Raven, which flew over the water, and never returned. Probably, the Raven found enough food floating in the water to satisfy it. After that, Noah sent out a Dove, just to to see if it could find rest on dry ground. The water was still very high, and the Dove returned to the window of the ark again.

Noah gently brought the Dove back into the ark in his hand. After seven days, he again released the Dove through the open window. Later, the bird arrived back with an Olive leaf in its beak. Noah knew that the water was down to tree level. A week passed, and Noah opened the window a third time, and released the Dove. The Dove never returned. Noah knew then that the flood was gone, and that the earth was drying up.

Noah released all the animals, birds and reptiles. He and his wife, and their sons, and their wives, all disembarked from the ship. The ark was empty. Noah had a special place in his heart for the beautiful Dove, which returned and brought him back the Olive leaf.

(In olden days the Olive Leaf was the symbol of peace. People at war would signify that they were asking for peace with their enemy, by carrying an olive branch. A king who carried an olive branch in his hand, meant that he had come to reign in peace).

God gave Noah a sign, that he would never again destroy all life. God placed a rainbow in the sky. The people of the Hebrew religion remembered God's promise, each time they saw a rainbow . Do you know the seven colours of the rainbow? (Violet, indigo, blue, green, yellow, orange, and red.)

Prayer:

> Father, we thank you for the birds
> We love the blue sky, the white clouds
> and the colours of the rainbow.
> We thank you for the black Raven,
> and for the peaceful Dove carrying the Olive leaf.
> Bring your peace into our world,
> and into our hearts.   Amen.

Hymn:

> You can't stop the rain from falling down. (J.P. 297)

Teachers' Note: (1) The Dove's return was a sign of better things to come. (2) When we return to school we can make it a better year than the previous one. (3) A fresh start is helpful. The story is found in Genesis Chapter 8. The questions which usually rise in telling the story are: (a) Noah's age, (six hundred years). This may be interpreted as six hundred Lunar months, with 13 in each year. (b) concerns the extent of the flood. Scientists have discovered that the ages of the remains of floods come from varying periods. For this reason, many teachers interpret the Genesis flood as as a "district flood."

(a) **Pipes and Dance**   *Week 2   Music*

Jenny's parents left Scotland to take up new employment. Jenny, and her younger brother Ian, moved with their parents to live in a new house, in a town in the North of England. They loved the beautiful hills near their home. Both Jenny and Ian were rather nervous about having to attend an English school. They had left all their young school-friends behind in Scotland.

On the first morning, they did not line up in the playground like the other children. Instead, their mother took them to meet the Head-teacher, who welcomed both of the children. He placed each of them in different classes, and introduced them to their new Teachers. The Teachers introduced Jenny and Ian to the children in the Worship assembly.

The Head-teacher asked Jenny and Ian whether they had any special talents: were they musical, or could they sing? Ian said that Jenny could dance the "sword dance". Jenny smiled, and said that Ian could play the chanter, and the bagpipes. The Head-teacher asked Ian, "What is a chanter?" Ian smiled, and answered, "Oh, it is the part of the bagpipes which makes the music. It is similar to the recorder, but narrower." The Head teacher asked Jenny and Ian if they would like to demonstrate before the other children in the assembly the following morning. The two children agreed to do so.

Next morning Jenny and Ian lined up in the school yard with the other school children. Both of them had a school bag, and each carried a second long black case. The English children were very curious to see what was inside the cases, but the Scottish children would not open them in the school yard. In the Worship Assembly, the Head-teacher invited Jenny and Ian to the front of the large room.

The children opened their black cases. Jenny took out two swords, and a tartan Tam O'Shanter hat with a red tassel on the top of it. Ian opened his long black case, and brought out a full set of bagpipes. Ian showed the Head-teacher the chanter part of the bagpipes. Jenny put her Tam O'Shanter hat on her head, and set the swords diagonally across each other on the floor. (Just like St. Andrew's cross.)

Ian's face became very red, as he blew air into the bag pipes. Then all at once the pipes began to drone, while Jenny held up her two hands in the air. Ian began to play the bagpipes, and Jenny began to dance across the swords, and between the swords. Back and forth she went, and her nimble toes never once touched the swords. Sometimes she was holding her hands above her head. Ian was piping with all his skill, and tapping his feet at the same time. The children in the assembly were delighted, and soon everyone was clapping their hands in rhythm to the bagpipe music.

After Jenny had finished her dance, and Ian had finished piping, the Head-teacher asked Ian whether he knew how to play the "Skye Boat Song." Ian said, "Yes, I can play it." The head-teacher announced the number of a hymn in the school hymnbook. Ian piped the tune, and the whole assembly sang a hymn about the Holy Spirit, to the tune of the. " Skye Boat Song".

Afterwards, all the children showed their appreciation by becoming really good friends to the two new Scottish pupils. *We should always try to be a friend to any new pupil at our school. Did you realise that someone may be lonely in a crowd?*

Prayer:

> Lord, we thank you for all kinds of music.
> For the organ in Church, and the piano in school.
> For brass bands and silver bands,
> and for all the instruments of the orchestra.
> For the bagpipes of Scotland and Ireland.
> For singing and for dancing.
> May we praise the Lord with joyful hearts.   Amen.

Hymn:

> Spirit of God. (C&P. 1. 63)

Teachers" Note: (1) First day attendance at school may make us feel lonely in a crowd. (2) Many children change schools at the beginning of a new school year. We all belong to each other, and we are members of a school family. (3) Have you noticed that music brings people together?

(b) The Pied Piper

Week 2   Music

Sometimes, there is a lesson to be learned from an old story, which we know, is only a story, and not actually true. Today, the children are about to hear the story, and then they will say afterwards, what lessons they have learned from it.

In part of what is now known as Germany (Westphalia), there was a town called Hamelin. The town was quite near the river Weser. Now, the people of Hamelin had a terrible problem. The town was plagued with rats. Rats came up out of the drains. Rats ran along the streets and into the houses and shops. Even the children could see rats in the school playground. The rats ran along the roof-tops of the buildings. If they scrambled out of the butchers shop, the rats would run into the bakery next door. They seemed to be appearing everywhere in Hamelin.

The rats ate the butter, cheese, bread, cream cakes, apple tarts, roast beef, and any other delicious food which they could find. They crawled into beds, and were found under the pews in the church. Everyone was displeased that the rats had increased to such a number. The citizens of Hamelin went to the mayor and town council, and demanded that the town council should find some means of getting rid of the rats. "We cannot stand rats in our town any longer," they said.

The town council promised to pay a large sum of money to anyone who could get rid of the rats from the town. One day, a rather strange looking man, dressed in yellow and red clothing walked in to the town hall. He carried a little musical pipe, like a flute or a recorder in his belt.

The "Pied Piper" as he was called, promised to clear the rats away for the towns-people, if the mayor and town council would agree to pay him one thousand guilders. The members of the town council gladly voted to pay the money to this strange looking man. Indeed, they would have done anything to be free from the plague of rats.

The Pied Piper took out the mysterious little pipe from his belt. He walked down the High Street playing a tune that no-one in the world had ever heard before. Robert Browning, the poet describes what happened next.

"To blow the pipe, his lips he wrinkled,
And green and blue his sharp eyes twinkled.
And ere three notes his pipe had uttered.
Out of the houses the rats came tumbling.
Great rats, small rats, lean rats, brawny rats,
Brown rats, black rats, grey rats, and tawny rats,
And step by step they followed him dancing,
Till they came to the river Weser."

No-one could believe their eyes. The mysterious music so charmed the rats, that they followed the Pied Piper in their thousands. He led them to the bank of the deepest part of the River Weser. The rats rushed into the river and they were all drowned; everyone of them! Then the Pied Piper came back for his payment.

When the mayor and members of the town council realised that the rats were gone forever, they refused to pay the one thousand guilders to the Pied Piper. "Go away to some other town," they said. "We will not pay you!"

The Pied Piper walked out, without saying another word. He had a strange look in his eyes. He took out his little pipe, and he walked down the High Street a second time. He played another beautiful and mysterious tune, sweeter than even the first tune had been. There was a great bustling sound, as all the children of the town came rushing out of the houses, and schools. They were laughing, and dancing down the High Street, behind the Pied Piper. He led the happy children towards the river Weser.

The town council members and the parents were frightened. Were the children going to be drowned, they wondered? Would the Piper dressed in his quaint red and yellow clothes, do such a thing? Then to everyone's relief, he turned away from the river, and led the happy parade of children to Koppelberg Hill.

A cave opened in the side of the hill, and the Pied Piper led them through the dark cave. When they came out on the other side of the hill, they went over yet another mountain. They reached the beautiful happy land of Transylvania, where they formed a children's colony there. They lived happy ever after. The parents never saw their children again. (Remember, this is only a story!)

Can you suggest any lessons to be learned from this story?

a) If you make an agreement, you ought to keep your part of the bargain.

b) You should not tell lies to visitors or to anyone else.

c) We ought to appreciate someone who genuinely helps us.

d) Children are worth more than any golden guilders.

Prayer:

> Lord, we thank you for old stories
> written down for us long ago.
> Help us to learn from them.
> We thank you for children.
> Teach us that every child
> is more valuable to God our Father,
> than all the wealth of the world.   Amen.

Hymn:

> Travel on, travel on, there's a river that is flowing. (J.P. 42.)

Teachers" Note: (1) The Pied Piper really wanted to be helpful. (2) The mayor and town council of Hamelin, in the story, were really very greedy people. (3) They did not keep their promise.

(c) Flutes and Funerals

Here is a story from the Bible about a funeral. It has a very happy ending! All religions have some kind of a funeral rite. A funeral is the last act of respect, that people perform, when someone they love dies.

The word, "funeral' begins with the letter "f". Can you think of anything which begins with the letter "f" connected with a funeral?

The first "f" is sure to be *"flowers."* People usually give beautiful flowers at a funeral. Long ago, there was another "f" connected with a funeral. It was *"feasting".* Usually, when someone died, a special meal was held for the relatives of the person who had died.

Now for a surprise! Did you know that in olden times *"flutes"* were often used at Eastern and Roman funerals? Flutes may have a peculiar shrill high pitched wailing sound, as if someone were crying. Musicians were paid to provide the sad music at a funeral.

There was once a crowd of people around Jesus. Just at that time, a Ruler by the name of Jairus arrived in a hurry. He said to Jesus, "My daughter has just died. Come quickly, and put your hand on her, and she will live." Jesus went along with the Ruler.

As Jesus was walking down the road with Jairus, a woman in the crowd, who had been very ill for twelve years, came up behind Jesus. She stretched out her hand and touched the edge of his cloak. She thought to herself. "If I could only touch his clothes, I would be healed." Jesus looked round and he saw her. He said to the sick woman, "Cheer up, your faith has healed you" From that very moment she was well!

Soon Jesus and the Ruler reached the house. He found that the funeral activities had already begun. A crowd had gathered inside the house. The flute players had begun to play their sad tunes. Some people were weeping and wailing. The first thing Jesus did was to send the flute players away. Then, he told the people who were weeping and wailing to leave. Lastly, he asked the crowd to go home.

Jesus said, "Why are you making such a fuss. The little girl is asleep. She is not dead" The people laughed at Jesus, because they did not believe him. He put everyone out of the house, except his three disciples, Peter, James, and John. He also allowed the little girl's father and mother to stay.

Jesus took the girl by the hand, and he said, "Little girl, get up." Instantly, the girl stood up, and walked around the room. She was twelve years of age. Jesus said, "Do not tell anyone about this. Give the girl a good meal, she must be hungry." Jesus left them and went off to help someone else.

The Gospels do not say what happened to the flute players. Maybe they did not go home after all! Perhaps, they just waited outside the house. Maybe, when the little girl appeared healthy and well again, the flute players changed their tune to happier music.

Sometimes, English clog dancers have one of their members playing a little flute, very like a tin whistle. They play a merry country dance tune, that makes us all feel happy. The pleasant thing about learning to play a musical instrument is that some day you may be able to express your own inner feelings , just as if you were a Sky-lark or a Nightingale!

Prayer:

> Lord, we are young and well.
> We thank you for good health.
> We pray for all sick children,
> Make them better from their illness.
> We love the instruments of the Orchestra.
> Bless all musicians whose music
> we are learning to enjoy.

Hymn:

> I danced in the morning. (C&P. 1. 22)

Teachers' Note: (1) The point of the story is that children may have faith in Jesus. (2) Jesus always had time for children. (3) It is true that the Flute may produce a sad tune, but it may also sound happy music, which makes us want to tap our feet, or clap our hands. Reference to Flute Players is only found in St. Matthew Ch.9. v23. (see also Mark. Ch.5. v35-43 ,and Luke Ch.8. v49-56).

(a) Danny's Cow-Bells

Week 3   Teams

Once upon a time, there was a lady and her husband, who had a very sick little boy, by the name of Danny. He was so ill that he had not been able to attend school for a long time. One day Danny's Mum was at a car boot sale. She saw a little glass bell for sale. The bell was very cheap, so she bought it for Danny.

The sick boy grew to love the tinkle of his little bell. Sometimes, he would ring the little glass bell, to call his mother, if she were in the next room. Everybody was happy, when Danny slowly became well again, and came back to school.

When the Summer holidays came round, Danny's parents decided that they all should have a good holiday. They arranged to fly to Switzerland for two weeks. Danny was excited about going in the train to the airport, and then flying above the clouds. When they reached Switzerland, they fell in love with the beautiful countryside, especially the mountains and the lakes.

On the following day, Danny and his Mum and Dad, were eating their picnic, high on the hillside beside a lake, when suddenly, they heard bells. This reminded Danny of his own little glass bell, and the time when he had been ill. He wondered how anyone could hear bells on the side of a mountain. Then a farmer came by, driving a herd of cows. The tinkling sound was made by the cows. Each cow had a bell on a strap tied around its neck.

Mum, Dad, and Danny put their heads together, and talked. "Wouldn't it be wonderful if we could buy enough bells to make up a Hand-bell Team for the children at the school back home?" So the family spent a lot of time, looking at the shops and agricultural stores, which sold such farm equipment as horses leather harness and cow-bells.

They knew that the bells which they had to find, must all have a different note, so that when anyone rang them, each bell would give a different and higher or lower note. The bells had to sound, as if someone were playing a piano, with their fingers going up the scale, higher and higher. Eventually, they bought twelve cow-bells.

When they returned to England, they gave them to the music teacher at the school. The Teacher was very pleased. She said that the bells were not exactly the correct tones, but that she could adapt each bell to suit. She made the straps, into handles for each bell. Then she put the twelve bells on the table in rows.

The Teacher chose twelve children, and each child was allotted a bell. The children stood around three sides of the long table. Large print music was put on a music stand. Each child rang a bell at the correct time, and then replaced it on the table.

A few months passed, then one morning in the Worship Assembly, everyone was delighted to hear the school Hand-bell Team play many tunes from their hymn-book. Children were ringing one bell, and sometimes two. As they rang individually, the 12 children sounded as if they were one Team playing in sweet harmony.

Danny thought to himself that being ill was just awful, especially having to stay in bed for such a long time! Yet something good came out of it all. He still kept his little glass bell at home by his bed-side. The Teacher had said to him, "Danny, large oak trees grow from little acorns." Do you know what she meant? (The Handbell team could be traced back to Danny's little glass bell).

Prayer:

> Good Lord of music, we thank you
> for the music of cow-bells in harmony,
> and for the pealing of Church bells.

We love the sound of birds that sing together,
and the bleating of little lambs that skip about.
Good Lord, receive the praise of school children
as they try to work together as a team. Amen.

Hymn:

The Bell of creation. (C&P. 2. 86)

Teachers' Note: (1) No-one likes to be ill. Yet, when we look back at illness afterward, we may see that some good happened. (Danny received his glass bell.) (2) The memory of the glass bell caused Danny to notice the sound of the cow-bells when on holiday. (3) Danny shared his love of bells with his school friends, who became members of the Hand-bell Team.

(b) The Football Team   *Week 3   Teams*

No doubt, you have taken part in a team of some kind. There are football teams, hockey teams, tug of war teams, and cricket teams. There are many other kinds of teams. Can you think of any? (Darts team, bowling team, dancing team, a team of Doctors and Nurses at a hospital operation; or even a team of horses on a farm.).

The main thing about being in a team, is that everyone works together for the good of the team. It is very sad to have a football team, and to find that one player will not pass the ball to other players. Perhaps, it is a boy or girl who wants to score all the goals by himself or herself. This is foolish selfishness. That kind of player spoils the chances of the team winning the match. A good team plays together.

There was a Primary school in the North of England, that had a very good football team. The children were all aged between eight years and ten years old. They lost some matches, but many they managed to win by skilful playing. They wore red and green football shirts, with white shorts. Their socks were red with green rings at the top. The girls and the boys at the school were all very proud of their very own football team. One day they had the opportunity of playing a Scottish school, just over the border, not far from Carlisle.

The Teacher said that all the players, and the supporters had to bring their own packed lunch with them. They had also to bring three pounds each to pay for the coach fare, and for one can of coke. Wayne raised his hand in the class, and told his Teacher that he would not be going, because his father was out of work. His family could not afford three pounds all at once.

The other members of the Team, who were playing, were most disappointed, because Wayne was such a good player. Terry, (who played in the full-back position, because he was tallest in the team), raised his hand.

"Please, Sir", he said, "I have an idea. Why don't we do without buying cans of coke this time. We could bring a paper cup each, and buy a couple of bottles of concentrated Orange Juice; the kind that may be diluted with water. We could easily get water from a tap in the dressing room. We could drink the diluted Orange Juice instead. If we did that, we could save the cost of a can of coke each. If we put the money we saved out of everyone's three pounds, then we could easily pay Wayne's coach fare, and we'd all have a Juice drink as well!"

Everyone in the class thought it was a good idea. They knew that Terry was good at maths as well as football. Terry could work out the cost of it all. So everyone agreed to carry out the plan. The Teacher agreed that it was a splendid idea.

When the day of the match arrived, the eleven players, (both boys and girls), and all their supporters from the school, boarded the coach. They travelled many miles up the motorway, past Carlisle, and over the Scottish border to the playing field, where they met the Scots Team. The football match turned out to be a tough one played on a good field.

The Scots Team wore a blue and white football strip. They were very good players, and they scored five goals. They knew how to pass the ball to each other. No one was silly enough to keep the ball to themselves. The English team tried very hard, and they managed to score four goals.

The Referee looked at his watch, and said, "There are only five minutes left to play!" Terry looked at Wayne, "Do not let the Scots beat us," he said. Indeed, the whole English Team looked at Wayne The ball was kicked up the field by Hasan, the outside right, to Angela. She quickly passed the ball onwards. Fortunately, Wayne was near the Scottish goal-posts. He saw his opportunity, and he kicked the ball perfectly, in the right direction.

The Scots Goal keeper tried to catch the ball, but he jumped to the left, instead of the right. Wayne smiled. The ball was in the Scottish Team's net. They had scored the equaliser, just a minute before the game ended.

The Referee blew his whistle. What a great game it was! Both schools had scored . Result 5-5. The Scots Team gave three cheers for the English Team, and the English Team gave three cheers for the Scots Team.

Then the surprise came! The Scots Teacher brought out from the coach, a great basket hamper of food, buns, biscuits, and would you believe it, cans of coke! Everyone was happy.

The English school boys and girls were tired after the match, and most of them slept a little on the coach, going homewards. Angela said to her team-mates.

"What a good team we are, and how wise we were to bring Wayne with us. He scored the last and vital goal!" Wayne felt a little shy. He just gave them a smile and a wink!

Prayer:

> Lord, we are happy when we are a Team.
> May we always play with fairness.
> May we never cheat at any game.
> Give us grace to do our best.
> Show us how to encourage each other.
> Teach us that if we lose, to be good losers.   Amen.

Hymn:

> The family of man. (C&P. 1. 69)

Teachers' Note: (1) The Team needs every member! Everyone is important. Every Team needs supporters to encourage the players. (2) The Team must share days of easy success, and days when the game is very difficult, and goals are especially hard to score. (3) A Team finds that life is full of good surprises when it shares the one spirit.

(c) The Big Coracle   *Week 3   The Team*

In the year 521, a baby boy was born into a wealthy family in Ireland, in a little place called Tirconnell in County Donegal. His parents being Irish Christians, named their baby, "Columba." The baby's family was related to Niall, who had been High King of Ireland.

We must understand that there were established churches and schools in Ireland, a long time before there were any in Britain. The boy, Colomba, grew up to be a Christian. He attended a very good school. Columba was taught by Irish Monks. They taught him several languages.

As a boy, Columba used to watch the fishermen building their boats, called "coracles" beside the sea. A coracle was made round, or shaped like a basket. The Irish fishermen built their coracles, from a framework of slender tree branches. Then, they wove around the frame, a basket-work of reeds, and grasses. A coracle was a little like a floating bird's nest.

The fishermen stretched animal skins inside the coracle to keep the water out. Last of all, they poured hot pitch (tar) over the inside of the coracle. When the tar had cooled and hardened, the coracle became water-tight. At sea, the crew used broad oars like paddles, or a small sail. The boy, Columba, thought to himself, "when I grow up, I will build a really big coracle, and sail far out into the sea."

Columba being a good scholar decided, that he would become a Priest in the Irish Church even though he had the fighting nature of a warrior. He loved the Lord Jesus with all his heart. He later founded two monasteries in Ireland.

A monastery was a large house built specially for Christian men. There were sleeping quarters, which were more like small cells. There was a refectory, which was a large dining hall. The monks usually sat around one long wooden table. The chief monk was called the Abbot, and he always sat at the head of the table.

While the monks were eating their meals, one of the monks sat in a special high chair apart from the table. He read out loud from the Bible or from a good book. There was also a church or chapel where the monks held regular services every day. A cloister was a covered stone passage-way, sometimes going around four sides of a square, where monks could walk around even in wet weather.

When Columba looked across the Irish Sea on a clear day, he could see the hills of Scotland. Columba remembered that as a boy he had watched the fishermen building the small coracles by the sea. He with twelve monk-companions set to work. They built a very large coracle, sturdy enough to sail across the waters which separated Ireland from Scotland.

In the year 563 Colomba and his twelve companions set sail for Scotland in their big coracle, stocked with food, manuscript books, and other goods. They eventually landed on the small island of Iona. On the island, Colomba and his friends, built the first Christian monastery in Scotland, with its church and school.

In those far off days, there were few places of learning. Iona became a famous Christian centre. Visiting pilgrims and scholars came to learn more. The small island became famous. Columba wrote hymns, and translated nearly three hundred books from other languages. We can understand just how well he had been taught as a boy. The monks increased in number as others joined them.

When the pilgrims visiting Iona returned to the mainland, they built churches in the villages. They helped to spread the gospel stories about Jesus among the people. Columba sent his Gaelic preachers and teachers all over Scotland, and also to the North of England. The Island of Iona became their first headquarters.

Soon, both Scotland and Northern England were to become Christian countries, as people began to believe in Jesus Christ. Previously, most people had never heard about Jesus. When people became Christians, they found that the building of schools generally followed the building of churches. Columba and his monks were really teams of Christians spreading the good news of the Gospel.

When Columba died, he was buried in the graveyard on Iona. The island later became a burial place for famous people. Since then, Forty-eight Scottish Kings have been buried there. Anyone may visit Iona, so maybe your parents will take you there some day on a holiday visit. In the years 1958 and 1959, archaeologists digging up the ground, found the stone cell (room) in which Columba used to live. The Church keeps a special Saint's day to remember St. Columba, on the 9th. June each year.

Now, a question to conclude our Worship Assembly. Does anyone know of a another good man, who also sailed in a boat with twelve friends? (Jesus with his twelve disciples).

Prayer:

> Heavenly Father, we thank you for St. Columba.
> We thank you for his twelve companions,
> who came to Britain to tell us about Jesus.
> We thank you for schools and learning.
> We thank you for hospitals and care of the sick.
> Bless all teachers and school children.
> Bless nurses and doctors.   Amen.

Hymn:

> Go tell it on the mountain. (C&P. 1 24) or (J.P. 65)

Teachers' Note: (1). St. Columba when a little boy liked to learn about anything. He really tried when at school. He learnt about boat building, stone masonry, sailing, and anything in books. (2). St. Columba learnt also to love the Lord Jesus in his heart. This is the most important fact about him. (3). St. Columba was a fierce Irish warrior by nature, but he became a true Christian. As a Leader he reminded many people of Jesus himself.

(a) The Green-Grocer's Shop   *Week 4   Harvest*

Preparations: *(In the front of the Assembly, a table represents a Green-Grocer"s shop. A few shopping bags, flowers, or vegetables are on display. Mr. and Mrs. Green wear a shop keeper's apron or coat. Individual children represent the vegetables on sale at Harvest time). For dramatic effect on the hearers, a pause is necessary between each verse. (Count a silent ten between each verse).*

Teacher: Today we are going to present the Harvest on view at any local green-Grocer's shop.

Individual Children:

1.   I am Mr. Green, this shop I own.
        All I sell, someone has grown.

2.   I am Mrs. Green, I weigh out the fruit.
        I put all in a bag, even beet-root!

3. I am a Potato, I don't make a sound.
    I grow very quietly under the ground.

4. I am a Carrot, you may eat for your dinner.
    If I grow very long, they say "I'm a winner!"

5. I am a Parsnip, the Carrot's brother.
    I am boiled and cooked, by everyone's Mother.

6. I am a Turnip, a lantern I'll be,
    at Hallow'een, for all to see.

7. I am a Cabbage, fit for a Queen.
    Inside I am white, but outside I'm green.

8. I am an Onion, I can make you cry,
    if you cut me open, and stand close by.

9. I am a Tomato, they argue about me.
    A fruit or a vegetable, which shall I be?

10. I am an Apple, rosy and red.
    Eat one every day, and you'll be well fed.

11. I am an Orange, round like a ball.
    They peel me, and squeeze me; a drink for all.

12. I am Grape, we grow in a bunch.
    We are sweet to eat, along with your lunch.

(Other fruit may be added to the list, depending on Pupils available).

Children repeat together:

All fruit began as little seeds,
Vegetables grew large, in spite of weeds.
They drank in the sun, they drank in the rain,
And they will come back in Spring again.
Thanks be to God for Harvest Store.
Thanks be to God forever more!

Hymn:

All things bright and Beautiful. (J.P. 6) (C&P. 1. 3)

Teacher: A Prayer

Lord of the harvest, hear our prayer.
We thank you for good soil, and good seed.
We thank you for sunshine and rain,
and for cold and heat:
for sowing and for reaping.
We pray for hungry people overseas.
Grant them a good Harvest this year. Amen.

Teachers' Note: Children may carry actual fruit or vegetables, or pictures of them, either drawn, or cut from magazines. Care must be taken to ensure that the pictures are large enough, to be seen from the back of the Assembly. Humour is part of the child's world. The hymn will restore the sense of worship, before the final prayer.

(b) **When the Harvest Failed**   *Week 4   Harvest*

I shall be dead and gone, when you hear my story. My name is Mr. Patrick Ryan. Let me tell you my story which begins in Ireland in the year 1847. There were six members in our Ryan family. We had four lovely children, Sean, Patrick, Brigid, and little Coleen. My wife, Roseleen Ryan,was a good mother to our family. I worked a little farm belonging to the Landlord, who lived at the big house, a few miles away.

Once each year, I had to to pay tenant's rent for the year to the Landlord. I managed to grow two fields of corn, which I sold in the market, and that money paid the farm-rent for yet another year. Most of my other fields were used for growing potatoes. The poor Irish people in those hard times mostly used potatoes for food. (Grain was the money crop, and potatoes were the food crop). The grain, such as corn, wheat, and barley were sold in Dublin, and sent by ship to England.

Our four children loved their little farm, because Ireland is a very beautiful country. They played happily with the other Irish children, many of whom were barefoot, since their parents could not afford to buy them shoes. We had heard about a disease affecting potatoes in other parts of Ireland, but we never took much notice. We were poor, but happy. Sean, Patrick, Brigid, and Coleen dearly loved their mother, who could make many tasty meals from potatoes.

One day when we were out walking round the edge of the potato field, the children smelt a horrible smell coming out of the ground. They ran back to tell me about it. I accompanied them along the field. The smell became stronger. I wrung my hands in despair.

"Children", I said, "Our farm has been infected by the Potato Blight. I have heard that this terrible potato disease has been in the farms in Europe, especially in Belgium. Now it is here in Ireland." The horrible smell was caused by the potatoes rotting in the ground. I wondered what we should do for food?" Our children did know how to answer.

It was true! Not only was our farm struck by the disease, but most other farms in our district also lost their entire potato crop. This Potato Blight eventually spread all over Ireland. The poor Irish people suffered from malnutrition, illness and starvation. Many of the poorest died in the years, 1845, 1846, 1847, and 1848.

The population of Ireland was then about eight million people, but because of hungry people dying, or others leaving the country, the population fell by one million people in five years. You see, the problem was that farmers always kept some of their potatoes back in store, as new seed-potatoes for the following year. Not only had the harvest failed, but we had no seed potatoes for next year. Disaster faced us. What could we do?

My wife, Roseleen and I talked it over, when the children went to bed that night. That year we decided not to sell our corn harvest. We decided to use it for food instead. We could make flour from the corn (oats). Our family continued to eat for another year, but we had to eat very small meals to make the food last.

We soon had no corn to sell, to pay the rent. The Landlord had sent us a threatening letter, which stated that we had either to pay our rent, or he would evict our family from our home and farm. The children were frightened. What could we have done?

I told the family that there was only one hope left. We would have to sell our horse, hens, and our one cow. Whatever furniture we owned, was only home made furniture, and it might bring us in a few pounds. If we sold up everything, we might have enough money to pay our fare, and be able to sail across the Atlantic Ocean, to Uncle Michael in America. We knew that he had a farm outside Boston. Many thousands of other Irish people were being forced to emigrate at that time.

Our family cried, as we closed the farm gate behind us, for the last time. We travelled to Dublin, and then we set sail for America. It was a long sea journey in the big sailing ship. After weeks at sea, we eventually sailed into Boston harbour. Some neighbour who had reached Boston in an earlier ship before us, had told uncle Michael, what was happening to our family.

Imagine our pleasure, as I stood with my wife, Roseleen, and our children, Sean, Patrick, Brigid and Coleen on the deck of the ship, when we first reached America. As we looked down at the quayside, something happened, which was like a miracle. We saw Uncle Michael waving up at us. The first thing we did when we put our feet on dry land, was that the whole Ryan family knelt down on the quayside, and we said a prayer, thanking God for our safe voyage. Everyone of us, including Uncle Michael said "Amen." Our family, when we reached America, felt like the Hebrews who had left Egypt, and had finally reached the "Promised land."

The American authorities sold us a tract of land, very cheaply, and we set up our own farm. We built our own log cabin farm house, with Uncle Michael's help. The soil turned out to be very good soil. We sowed wheat, corn, and many kinds of green vegetables. We ploughed a special field for growing the, "Irish potato." We have been so happy in America, that after a time, we had forgotten all about our sad experiences in the dreadful famine year of 1847, when the potato harvest failed. Uncle Michael was our friend and helper. Thanks be to God!"

Prayer:

> Good Lord, we pray for the poor nations
> of the third world.
> We pray for countries overseas,
> where the harvests may have failed.
> Grant wisdom to their governments,
> that farmers may learn to produce
> the best crops from the soil.
> Teach us, as children to be thankful.   Amen.

Hymn:

> I planted a seed. (C&P. 2. 134)

Teachers' Note: (1) We take the potato harvest for granted. (How many kinds of meal can be made from potatoes?) (2) The harvest failed, even though the Ryans were a hard working family (3) Notice, that the Ryans thanked God for a safe sea journey. They never gave up hope, and were willing to work a new farm . (The potato "Blight" was officially named , "Phytophthora infestans.")

(c) Four Kinds of Harvest

Jesus told a parable about a farmer, who sowed his wheat, and the seeds fell on four kinds of soil.

The Four Sowings:

The Farmer sowed the seed, and some fell by the wayside, and the birds came down, and ate up the seed.

The Farmer sowed seed, and some fell on stony ground, where it had not much depth of earth. The seed grew quickly, but because the plants did not have deep roots, the sun scorched them and they died.

The Farmer sowed his seed, and some fell among thorns, and the thorns grew up and choked the plants. Again, the wheat died.

The Farmer sowed the seed, and some fell into good ground. It produced a very good harvest. The cereals increased, some by a hundred per cent more, some by sixty per cent more, and some by thirty per cent more. The Farmer had a very good harvest from the fourth sowing.

Four kinds of Listeners:

This story will explain what the parable means. See if you can link the parable of the four sowings to the four young people in the following story.

There was a good Youth leader, who ran the village Youth Club. He had been a soldier, so the young people gave him the nick-name, "Captain". He was an expert gym instructor. Captain could vault over the gym-horse, better than any of the young people. Usually, when the Club met, he would talk to the members, at some point in the evening. Captain was never boring to listen to. The young people really admired him.

Sometimes he would talk about walking with a straight back, and not slouching. Other times he would talk about the need to keep our teeth clean. He would give hints on how to climb hills, or what clothes and footwear to buy for an adventure holiday. He often urged the club members not to begin to smoke, because smoking harmed the lungs. He discussed why some young people became vandals and destroyed public property.

Captain, said he that believed in three desirable things. They were a healthy body; an understanding mind; and a quiet spirit.

Susie was one of the young people, who was a bit giddy. She usually let Captain's instructions go in one ear and out the other. When Captain was talking to the teenagers at the pool, Susie was listening to somebody else. Susie pushed a younger girl into the pool. The Pool Superintendent was very angry, and ordered her to leave the pool, and to get dressed. "We will not have you back in this pool. You are just a bully," he said to Susie. The other young people said, "If only Susie had listened to what Captain was saying!"

Garry, was another good lad, but he really was a show-off. He would volunteer to do tasks, but often gave up, and left them half-done. Captain asked a member to volunteer to wash the windows of the Youth Club Coach. Garry offered to do the job. He washed the coach windows inside, but because his favourite television programme was about to begin, he slipped away home, and left the outside of the windows unwashed. Next day, when the club members arrived to go to the Bowling Alley, they found that the coach had dirty windows. Worse still, Garry had left the water tap running all night. Some of the members had to wash the windows themselves. Everyone was late at the Bowling Alley that morning. Garry usually responded immediately to what he was told, but he gave up too easily!

Tracy was another lovely person, but she was one of those people, whom we call a "worrier." Captain knew that her handwriting was beautiful. He asked Tracy to become the Secretary of their club. Tracy accepted the position. After she went home, she realised what she had done. She had become the club Secretary! Tracy worried in the morning, she worried in the afternoon, and she worried at night, even when she was in bed! She thought that she might not be good enough. She might not be able to spell everything correctly. At last, she could bear the worry no longer. Tracy resigned. She gave it all up. Worry had robbed her of her confidence, despite everything Captain had said to encourage her.

Peter, was an ordinary member of the Club. He realised that Captain, their Youth Leader, was a reliable person, who always spoke the truth. Peter always listened to his Leader. He always tried to to improve himself. He tried to become a good runner, and an expert on the parallel bars in the gym. He, also tried to cultivate Captain's third virtue, which was, "a quiet spirit." Sometimes, he felt a little panic on the inside, but he always managed to control his fears.

When Mrs. McClements accidentally set her chip pan on fire, she ran out into the street screaming. Peter heard her, and ran into her kitchen. He put a dish cloth under the water tap until it was wet. He quickly wrung the wet cloth out, and put the damp cloth over the frying pan. The flames deprived of air, went out. When people asked Peter, how he knew what to do? Peter said that he listened to Captain at the Youth Club.

Peter regularly went to Church on a Sunday, because Captain had told him that attending morning service was a help in guarding a quiet spirit. Peter, when he became older, went to the Sixth Form College, and he later became a Para-Medic in the ambulance service. He seemed to have a lot of practical medical knowledge at accidents. Most of all, he was able to calm people down. Captain was very proud of the young people who passed through his Youth Club.

Did you spot the four kinds of listeners? Did you understand that Jesus was very like a good Youth Leader? The story is about the harvest we all reap in our own lives.

Prayer:

>Lord, we thank you for the Farmers, who sow the seed.
>We also thank you, for people who tell us the truth.
>Help us to pay attention to the words of the Bible,
>and to any Leader who tries to lead us
>in pure and useful ways.
>Above all, may we take Jesus as our example.   Amen.

Hymn:

>Pears and Apples, wheat and grapes. (C&P. 2. 135).

Teachers' Notes: (1) The different types of soil represents the various types of listeners. (2) The seed is the spoken or written truth, especially as that taught by Jesus. (3) We may become true followers of our Leader, by paying attention to his teaching. (see Mark Chap. 4.)

(a) The Conker Tree

Not far from the village school, there was a gigantic tree. The village children called it the "Conker Tree" because each year they collected conkers from it. Pat, one of the children, took five leaves on one stem, to the village library. She found a book on British Trees. She compared her stem with the five leaves with pictures of trees in the book, until she found the correct one. Then she came back to the other children, and told them, "That tree is not called a Conker Tree, its proper name is a Horse Chestnut tree."

The children did not attempt to eat the fruit of the Horse Chestnut tree. They usually made a hole in the beautiful brown chestnuts, and put a string through them. One girl or boy held up the string, with the chestnut on it, and the other hit it with all their might. They had a lot of fun from playing at conkers. The other player who had been holding the string, also had a turn at striking the chestnut .

The tree really was very old, and very beautiful. It was covered in thousands of green leaves, and high up on its branches, hundreds of round green fruits with spikes on them were growing. The children knew from past practice, that when they peeled away the spiked shell of the fruit, that they would find the conkers inside.

The village policemen had warned the children that they must stop throwing sticks, and stones at the Horse Chestnut tree, trying to knock down the conkers. He said that because the tree was just behind the stone wall on the village green, that someone would eventually get hit with a stick or stone as they were passing by. He said that there was a rhythm in Nature, and that the the conkers would only fall at the proper time.

He said that when they eventually fell, the children could easily gather them as they lay on the ground. They were spoiling the environment, by breaking the branches and leaves off the old tree. The children just waited until the policeman went away, and then they again began to throw up sticks, trying to knock down more conkers.

Pat loved Natural things, so she felt that she ought to keep away until the tree dropped its fruit. She noticed that the leaves of the tree had changed from being a beautiful green colour to a golden yellow. She thought to herself, that it would not be long, until the leaves and fruit fell off.

After school was over, on the way home, once again, a number of of the children, began to throw sticks and stones up at the tree, regardless of their having being warned about it being a dangerous practice. Ralph, a year five boy, could not find a suitable stick to throw, so he took half a brick in his hands, and threw it up into the tree. When the half brick came falling down, it narrowly missed Sean, who was standing on the wall, but it struck Lucy in the face, breaking her glasses.

People standing nearby had to phone for an ambulance. Everyone was afraid that some of the broken glass might have gone into Lucy's eye. Ralph felt very guilty, because he had already been warned about his action. Fortunately, the Hospital Doctor who examined Lucy, declared that no glass had entered the eye. Her spectacles, however, had been broken beyond repair. All the other children who had been throwing sticks knew that they had been very foolish. This event made the children stay away from the tree.

A week after the accident, there were two days of heavy rain-storms. When everyone was grumbling about the bad weather, Pat, the young naturalist, smiled. "Let us now, all get down to the Horse Chestnut tree after school," she suggested.

When the children arrived at the tree, they realised that Pat was right. The heavy rains had beaten against the branches of the old tree. The yellow leaves had fallen to the ground. The green spiky covers of the conkers had fallen apart, when they had fallen to the ground. There seemed to be hundreds of beautiful brown chestnuts lying everywhere on the grass and on the path. They were even wedged in the stones on the wall.

Each boy and girl gathered enough conkers in their school bags for themselves. Pat was a thoughtful girl. She gathered two plastic bags of Conkers; one for Lucy who was not yet back at school, and one bag for herself. She intended next Spring to plant a chestnut into a pot of soil, just to see whether it would grow a Horse-Chestnut plant or not.

The children were beginning to understand what the, "rhythm of Nature" meant now. *"Rhythm" is about movement and resting. They had not needed to throw up sticks at the trees. Instead, they should have waited for the chestnuts to fall themselves. Everything in the natural world has its own time. A time to sow; a time for growing; a time to reap; a time for green leaves; and a time for Autumn tinted yellow leaves; and lastly, a time to rest in Winter. The environment is another name for God's wonderful world.*

Prayer:

> Our Heavenly Father,
> For the glory of Autumn colour, we thank you.
> For the change, from green to brown and gold,
> we praise you.
> For harvest of the soil, and fruits of the trees,
> we bless you.
> Lord, accept our Assembly Worship.   Amen.

Hymn:

> Autumn days when the grass is jewelled. (C&P. 1. 1)

Teachers' Notes: (1) The Rhythm of Nature brings us to the Autumn period with its glorious colours, and later to Spring with its greenery. (2) Pat was interested in finding out the name of trees, by reading in the Library. (3) The other children were disobedient for a time, and disobedience brings its own results. However, the children later understood, and tried to fit in with Nature's rhythm.

(b) The Red Squirrels   *Week 5   Autumn Environment*

Today,we have to think very hard, because the question is, "In what ways are school-children like red squirrels?" (Red squirrels are really a red-brown colour).

It was the month of October. The red squirrels had come to the grounds of the big Manor House, because they had to move to a new area. There were so many Grey squirrels, in the forest where they used to live, that they were frightened away. For some strange reason, Red squirrels and Grey squirrels never live together for very long. The Red squirrels had kept moving on, after the Spring time had passed. During the hot Summer, they seemed to want to move Northwards. They had travelled many miles, until they reached the woods around the Manor House. It was a suitable place for Red Squirrels, with plenty of trees and food around. The squirrels decided to remain in this Northern English forest.

There was quite a colony of them. During the Summer, they had a wonderful time, swinging from branch to branch, and never once falling off. This year's berries, and last year's nuts were in plentiful supply, so they were never hungry. Sometimes, they would climb on to the roof of the Manor House, and slip under the eaves, and make a nest among the rafters. Other times they kept to the high trees, to avoid the cats and dogs which sometimes roamed about.

When the Autumn arrived, the older squirrels usually instructed the younger ones. One wise old squirrel said, "Now you young squirrels pay attention to what I am going to say. This month begins what is called the 'Autumn'. It is the loveliest time of the year for squirrels. Because the Winter will soon be here, when the leaves and nuts fall to the ground. We as good squirrels, must learn three things; (1) to collect; (2) to store; (3) to remember!"

The younger squirrels, repeated in chorus, for they could not sing, "Collect; store; remember!" Off they went for a race up the Beech tree, across the Chestnut tree, across the house-wife's washing line at the Manor House, over the garden shed, and conservatory, and back up the Oak tree. They were out of breath before they all arrived high up, and safe and sound. It was fun being a squirrel in the Autumn time.

The Beech tree began to drop its nuts on the ground. The Chestnuts began to fall on the grass. The Oak tree dropped hundreds of acorns all over the driveway, which led to the Manor House. Plums, damsons, and apples were clinging to trees in the old Orchard. Now, as if remembering the old squirrel's words, they began to collect and carry, acorns, chestnuts, and nuts to little hiding places in the ground, or high up in the trees. Falling leaves of brown, yellow and gold colours were lying everywhere.

As the days became windy, and shorter, the squirrels went up to their nests, and went into deep sleep. When on very cold Winter days they became hungry, they used their little brains to "Remember," where they had hidden and stored their precious food supply. Down the Oak tree, along the clothes line, behind the garden shed, near the conservatory, there was a big stock of acorns. If squirrels preferred beech nuts for their breakfast, then they knew that behind the Holly tree, they had hidden a secret hoard. They had to beware of the black cat, and the two dogs, but as long as a tree was nearby, they could always escape.

*Now, for the question, **"In what way are school-children like Red squirrels?** Well, I'll tell you. Red squirrels need to collect, store and remember nuts for food. School children need to collect, store and remember knowledge.*

*   **First, we must "Collect" our knowledge.** This means that in class we should learn as much as we can. We may also attend our church, read books and study our environment.*

*   **Second, we must Store our knowledge.** The best place to store our learning is in our minds. We may write it in our exercise books. We may say it in poetry, or sing it in hymns and songs.*

*   **Third, we must Remember our knowledge.** We can all practise trying to remember what we did yesterday, or try to recall something important, which we learnt last week. A good way is to to use our imagination. Faith is full of good imagination. For squirrels, acorns and nuts are food. For school children, facts and figures are food for thought."*

Prayer:

> Father God, we love the antics of squirrels.
> They are so like children at play.
> Thank you, Lord, for the world of nature.
> Thank you for the changing seasons.
> May we like the squirrels,
> Collect, store and remember,
> our garthered knowledge.   Amen.

Hymn:

> All the animals that I have ever seen. (C&P. 2. 80).

Teachers' Notes: (1) Squirrels remind us of children at play. (2) Squirrels are hoarders. All kinds of knowledge are always worth hoarding in our minds. (3) Squirrels remember to use their hidden hoards when necessary. Knowledge is ours to use later on in life. "Knowledge" is a theoretical concept. (Care needs to be taken that this lesson is kept as 'concrete' as possible, so that children may understand.)

(c) The Autumn of Old Age   *Week 5   Autumn Environment*

The Spring-time of life is when we are young. The Summer of life is when we have grown up and we are at the height of our powers. The Autumn of Life is when we grow old. Eli, the Priest at the Jewish Temple at Shiloh, had reached the Autumn of his life. He was growing old. His eye-sight and his hearing were weakening, just as today older people often need glasses or hearing aids.

One day, a lady named Hannah was praying in the Temple. She and her husband had no family. She promised God, that if he would answer her prayer, to have a baby boy, that she would give the child back to the service of God. In time, a child was born in the family, and her husband reminded her of her promise to give the child to God's service. Hannah named the baby, "Samuel," because she had asked him of the Lord. When the baby grew older, Hannah brought the little boy to Eli, the Priest.

Hannah said to Eli, "I am the woman who was praying in the temple for a son. This baby was born to me. Therefore, I have lent my child to the Lord. As long as he is alive, he belongs to God." This is how Samuel came to live with Eli the Priest. Eli taught the boy Samuel from his childhood. As Samuel grew up, each year, his mother, Hannah, used to bring him a little coat which she had made for him.

Samuel helped old Eli who was the Minister in the Temple. Eli's eyes weakened so much, that he became blind. One night, when Samuel was asleep in the Temple, God spoke to the boy in a vision. "Samuel, Samuel," the voice called. The boy answered, "I am here". Samuel ran to Eli, and said to him, "Here I am , you called me." Eli said to Samuel, "I did not call you, go back to bed."

Samuel went back to his bed. "Again, God called, "Samuel". The boy ran in to Eli, a second time, and said, "Eli, you called me." Again, Eli answered, "I did not call, my Son, go and lie down."

In the darkness, God called a third time, "Samuel!" The boy ran to Eli, and said, "Eli you did call me." The old Priest realised it was the Lord who was calling Samuel. He said, "Go and lie down, and if you hear the voice again, you are to say, Speak Lord for your servant is listening."

Samuel, heard the voice calling him, and he answered as he had been told to do. "Speak Lord, for your servant is listening." Then, God gave Samuel a message for Eli. "Because Eli's sons had become wicked men, and were doing evil, God would remove them from power in the land."

The boy lay until morning, as he did not want to give Eli such a sad message. However, Eli called Samuel. He told the boy that he was to deliver the message to him from God, and if he kept any part of the message back, then God would punish him. So Samuel gave old Eli, the sad message that God had rejected Eli's evil sons in power in the land. Eli said to Samuel, "It is the Lord who has spoken to you. Let God do whatever seems right." Samuel, who was in the Spring-time of his life, continued to serve Eli, who was in the Autumn of his life.

All young people should try to help their Grandad, or Grandma in whatever way they can. Samuel also served the Lord with all his heart. Probably, he filled up the Temple lamps with fresh oil. Maybe, he polished the brass vessels. He always guarded Eli, in the evening, until the old man was fast asleep. Christians believe that we should always obey the Lord in everything we do.

Prayer:

Father, God, we thank you for young people,
who are in the Spring-time of life.
We thank you for strong parents,
who are enjoying the Summer of life.
We pray for older friends,
who are in the Autumn of life.
Grant that we may all serve the Lord,
and serve each other.   Amen.

Hymn:

Hushed was the evening Hymn. (J.P. 85)
or, Give me oil in my lamp. (C&P. 1. 43)

Teachers' Note: (1) Some children may ask about the "Winter" of life. They should be answered honestly. (2) Samuel was a servant of the Lord, just as much as Eli was. Both offered faithful ministries. (Did different tasks). (3) Prayer is not just speaking to God, but allowing God to speak to us by his Spirit in our minds and consciences.

(The following six Assemblies may be used as a two week series on the theme of the Lord's Prayer. Alternatively, they may also be used as individual Assemblies at various points of the school year.)

(a) Practising the Presence

Usually, we say the Lord's Prayer from memory. It is a *FAMILY PRAYER*. It does not say, "I, or me, or mine". It says, "We, and our, and us." The Lord's prayer can be divided up into TWO sections.

First, there is a section about God.

Secondly, there is a section about Ourselves.

The first part of the Lord's Prayer, helps us to practise the presence of God.

You may have heard someone practising playing the piano, or you may have seen an actor, or an actress practising standing perfectly still, just like a statue. Have you ever watched the long legged bird, called a "Heron?" It practises standing still on one leg, for a very long time. It is difficult to believe that it is alive. So one may practise an action until that action comes naturally. Now, when we are saying the Lord's Prayer, we are *"practising the presence of God"*.

Our Father who is in Heaven. It was the Lord Jesus who taught us to call God "Our Father." Many people thought of God as being an angry judge. However, when Jesus himself was praying, he called God, "Abba" which is a little like the word, "Daddy". God loves all of us, because we are all his children. Every girl and boy, in the world, may pray to God, because he is really "Our Father," and we all belong to "God's family."

Hallowed be your name. This means that we are to keep God's name holy, (differently). In Bible times, the name of a person often referred to their character. The Ten Commandments tell us not to "take God's name in vain". Some people use the name of God as a swear-word. "Hallowed be your name," means that we are to respect the name of God.

Your Kingdom come, Your will be done on earth, as it is in heaven, means that God is like a good king, who rules over a kingdom. God's kingdom is God's rule.

When people are unkind, God's rule says "Be Kind".
When people steal, God's rule says, "Do not steal."
When people tell lies, God's rule says, "Be truthful".

Now a story to explain these three points. Bobby and Jenny were brother and sister. They did not have a Dad because he had died in hospital the previous year. Yet they always said their prayers at bed-time, because their Dad had taught them to practise the presence of God. Each day they said the Lord's Prayer, because God was their Heavenly Father. They knew that God watched over them.

Bobby and Jenny had a school friend down the street, called "Terry." He often swore, using bad language, and used God's name in vain. One afternoon, Terry stole a can of lemonade from the village shop. Bobby and Jenny had a terrible problem on their hands. Should they continue to play with a boy who was a thief, or should they have nothing to do with him. They decided to tell Terry that they would not be playing with him any more, because he was a thief. Terry just swore at both of his school friends.

Terry did not know that the village shop had a television camera focussed on the customers. So next day, the Police car stopped outside Terry's house. A lady police officer, and a police-man asked to speak to Terry and his parents. They told Terry that the camera had recorded him actually stealing the can of lemonade.

Terry was frightened, and he admitted the crime. He said that he would never do such a thing again. His parents were very angry with him. The Police officers wrote his name in their book, and told Terry that they would keep it on their computer records. "You have a black mark against you, Terry," they said, "We will let the matter pass this time," and away they went in their car.

Terry told Bobby and Jenny what had happened. Terry said that he felt very guilty inside. Bobby said to Terry, that God, our heavenly Father knows everything we do, even if the camera had not been there. So, Terry never stole again. At night, before going to sleep, he began to say the Lord's Prayer. Terry practised the presence of God. It made him feel safe, and happier to know that everyone has a loving heavenly Father.

Prayer:
> The Lord's Prayer.

Hymn:
> Our Father who art in heaven. (J.P. 192) or (C&P. 1. 51)

Teachers' Note: (1) God is the loving Father of everyone. (2) To pray is to practise God's presence. (3) Anyone may pray, if they try.

(b) Food and Forgiveness

Week 6   The Lord's Prayer

The Second part of the Lord's Prayer is about ourselves. It helps us to realise our own need.

The need for food. (Give us this day our daily bread.)

Although the prayer mentions "daily bread" it really means "daily food." Children do not usually think about who provides their food. They just eat it up! Li Chang and his sister Sue Chang, lived with their parents in far away small island near Borneo. They were rather poor. In the rainy season, when the water in the fields was up to their ankles, their father and mother would plant short green rice plants.

In the hot wet climate, the rice grew up quickly. Mr. and Mrs. Chang and family harvested the rice, and brought it home. Sometimes they were so poor that they only ate a handful of cooked rice every day. Li and Sue were often hungry. They used to pray that God would send them hot wet weather, so that they could plant more rice.

Children in Britain would not like to have to eat rice for every meal. In many parts of the world, rice is people's main food. Everyone has a need for food. That is why we pray, give us this day our daily bread. To Li and Sue Chang, rice was their daily bread.

The need for forgiveness. (Forgive us our trespasses.)

Wrong actions, or wrong words, or wrong thoughts are called "trespasses" in the Lord's Prayer. Here is a story to illustrate what we mean by trespasses and forgiveness. There was a lovely little river which flowed through the town park. The swans, ducks and water hens swam up and down in it, all day long. Little fish called "sticklebacks" lived among the large stones in the river. Toads and frogs sat in the grass along its bank. It was a happy little place.

Sam coming home from school one day, found an old dirty paint drum, with sticky looking liquid inside it. He opened the screw top, and poured the sticky liquid into the little stream. He did not realise it, but he had poisoned that stretch of the river, The sticklebacks died and floated away down the river. The sticky liquid clung to the ducks' feathers. The swans became very sick. The frogs also began to die

All that week, Sam was very unhappy, because he knew what harm he had done. He desperately wanted to tell someone whom he could trust. Sam could not sleep at nights, he felt so guilty. He decided to tell the Vicar. The Vicar was a young man full of fun. However, he became very serious, when he heard Sam confess that he had poisoned the river. "Let us ask God to forgive you your trespass", he said. So Sam prayed, and asked God to forgive him.

Now the Vicar said, "Maybe the best thing that could happen, is that we might get a few days heavy rain. The rain would fill up the river, and wash away the poison." Next morning, sure enough, Sam awoke to the sound of heavy rain beating against the window pane! The rain came, as if by accident. It had nothing to do with Sam's prayer for forgiveness. Yet, it came at the right time. Faith is a mystery! God works all things together for our good.

Sam was really glad. It rained all day, and the rain washed the sticky liquid away down the river. The Vicar met Sam coming home from school that day. He smiled at Sam and said, "Have you noticed that the ducks and the swans are back in the park river again." Sam looked and sure enough they were! Sam knew that God had forgiven him his trespasses.

Prayer:

    The Lord's Prayer.

Hymn:

    I've got peace like a river. (C&P. 2. 143)

Teachers' Note: (1) We take our daily meals for granted. (2) There are inward spiritual needs. (guilt). (3) We cannot forgive ourselves.

(c) Big Brothers Forgive   *Week 6 The Lord's Prayer*

The basis of forgiveness. (Forgive us our trespasses, as we forgive those who trespass against us.)

Two boys were brothers. The older brother, Peter went to the High School, and the younger brother, Richard, went to the Primary school. Their mother was a widow and went out to work every day at the super-market. One evening, Richard, opened a tin of white paint, and foolishly painted the heels of his big brother's school shoes. Richard thought it was a funny thing to do, while really, it was a stupid prank. His older brother Peter was nearly late for the High School next morning, because he had to spend so much time trying to get the white paint off the heels of his shoes.

That very afternoon, young Richard was coming home from school, and it had been raining heavily. Very foolishly, he walked across the clay hill. He slipped and fell on the wet clay. His shoes were filthy with red sticky mud clinging to the soles. His socks were also dirty. He arrived home and walked over the carpet. What a mess he left behind him!

Meanwhile, Peter arrived home from the High School. He saw the muddy state of Richard's shoes and socks. He helped Richard to clean his shoes, and he polished them for him. Peter then washed his socks and hung them out to dry on the clothes line. Peter being the older, of the two boys, realised that his mother would not have time to look after young Richard's shoes and socks.

Soon everything was back to normal again. The black school shoes were on the shelf, ready for school next morning. Something puzzled young Richard. He said to Peter, " I thought that, 'Tit for tat was fair play' . Why did you clean and polish my shoes, and wash my socks, when I made such a mess of your shoes with that white paint? I expected you to say "That serves your right, you silly boy." I did wrong to you, but you did not try to get your revenge on me."

Peter smiled at his younger brother. He said, "I try to forgive people, especially my brother! Why don't you learn this little proverb. Do unto others, as you would have them do unto you."

This is what Jesus meant, in the Lord's Prayer when he said, "Forgive us our trespasses, as we forgive those who trespass against us."

Prayer:

The Lord's Prayer.

Hymn:

Make me a channel of your peace. (C&P. 2. 147) or (J. P. 161)

Teachers' Note: (1) To seek revenge is natural, even for a child. (2) Forgiveness is sweet to those who are forgiven. (3) Forgiveness carries healing between offender and the offended.

(a) Daniel in the Lions' Den   *Week 7   The Lord's Prayer*

Lead us not into temptation, but deliver us from evil.

This means, "Do not put us to the test", but deliver us from evil, (or from the evil one).

King Darius ruled over Babylon. He appointed Daniel as his most senior ruler, very like a Prime Minister. The other Junior Rulers (Satraps) planned evil against Daniel. They were jealous that Daniel seemed to be the King's favourite Ruler. These jealous Rulers came to King Darius and they pretended to honour the king.

They all shouted, "O King Darius, live for ever!" They suggested that King Darius should pass a law, that for thirty days, no-one in the country should pray to any god or man. No-one was to ask any request, except from the King. The Junior Rulers suggested that if anyone did pray, or ask such a request, that that person should be thrown into the lions' den. The lions were usually very hungry, and would have eaten up anybody in a short time.

King Darius did not know of the evil intentions of his Rulers, so he signed the decree, that no-one should pray for thirty days. The other Rulers knew that the law of the Medes and the Persians once passed, could not be changed.

When Daniel knew that the decree had been signed, he went into his house, which had windows open towards the far away holy city of Jerusalem. In his room he prayed to the Lord, giving thanks, three times each day, just as he had always done. The other Rulers came to King Darius and said, "O King, did you not pass a decree that no-one should pray to his god. Well, Daniel, the Chief Ruler prays three times each day."

King Darius, realised that the law of the Medes and Persians could not be changed for anyone. He argued for a time with his Rulers, trying to save Daniel from death. However, the law had to be obeyed. So King Darius was compelled by his own laws, to send soldiers to arrest Daniel.

The King said to Daniel, "May your God rescue you." The soldiers threw Daniel into the lions' den. They set a great stone at the entrance.

All that night, King Darius could not sleep, for thinking about Daniel. Early next morning, he went to the lions' den. He shouted, "Daniel, servant of the living God, are you alive? Has the God you serve, been able to save you from the lions?"

Daniel shouted back, "O King, live for ever! My God sent an angel to shut the lions' mouths. See, they have not harmed me, because I was innocent of doing anything wrong." The King was very happy, indeed, and he ordered that Daniel be brought out of the lions' den. There were no lions' teeth marks on Daniel, not even a tiny scrape, because Daniel trusted in his God, and knew how to pray.

This story will explain the passage in the Lord's Prayer, "Lead us not into temptation, but deliver us from evil." (Put us not to the test, but deliver us from evil one). Daniel might have been tempted not to say his prayers, and so escape being put among the lions. Yet, Daniel did say his prayers, because he was a thankful person. God saved Daniel from the lions and the wicked plan of the other evil Rulers.

Children should keep away from fierce wild animals, just as they must not go near guard dogs. Most of these animals mark out their own territory, and they will attack anyone who enters it. Not all animals can be trusted.

Daniel was severely tested. In the Lord's prayer, it is a normal human feeling to ask God not to test us too harshly. The good thing to remember, is that when God tested Daniel, he provided a way of escape.

Prayer:

The Lord's Prayer.

Hymn:

Who put the colours in the rainbow. (C&P. 1. 12) or (J.P. 288)

Teachers' Note: (1) Daniel prayed, because he had been taught to be thankful. (2) Daniel, was normal. He had fear, like anyone else. He would not go carelessly near a wild animal. (3) It is good, if we can pass our test, and resist a temptation.

(b) When Queen Victoria Stood   *Week 7   The Lord's Prayer*

The Kingdom, the Power and the Glory.

The writer of the Gospel of St. Matthew ends the Lord's Prayer with a doxology, "For thine is the kingdom, the power and the glory". These words are not to be found in the earliest manuscripts. (Hand-written copies of the Gospel).

A Doxology is a form of repeated words giving praise to God, which are said, or sung by a choir after a prayer.

A story will explain the meaning of these words. George Frideric Handel, (1685-1759), was the son of a clergyman, living in Saxony. As a boy of eleven years, he could play the organ, the harpsichord, the violin, and the oboe. The little German boy really loved musical instruments.

Later he studied music and became a famous composer. He wrote many oratorios. Most of these were based on characters (people) from the Old Testament. When the King of England held a royal water party on the river Thames (1717), Handel wrote his famous "Water Music"to entertain the wealthy people, who were floating on the royal barges.

His most famous oratorio was named, "The Messiah". The Messiah was sung for the first time, in the year 1742, by a huge choir in Dublin. (Nowadays, you may hear it on television at Christmas time, or at Church.)

About a hundred years later, after George Handel had died, Queen Victoria became the Queen of Great Britain. If you look at an old map of the world, you will see that many countries are coloured red. These countries were part of the British Empire, and ruled by Queen Victoria. So she was a very powerful Queen. Just think of it! She ruled India, Canada, Australia, New Zealand, South Africa, and many other parts of the world, as well as England, Ireland, Scotland and Wales.

Now, Queen Victoria as a young girl, did not really like Handel's music. She thought it was rather heavy and tiresome music. Being young she loved lighter music. Indeed, before she died, she left orders that Handel's music was not to be played at her funeral.

However, on one occasion, the Queen went along to hear the Messiah being sung. The choir was accompanied by an Orchestra. There are different parts of the oratorio, each sung by different singers. There are also parts called "choruses," which are sung together by every member of the choir. The most famous chorus of all is called the "Hallelujah" chorus.

In the crowded Opera House, people came to listen to the concert. Queen Victoria sat in the Royal Box, where she was seen by everyone else. The orchestra began by playing the National anthem, "God save the Queen." Everyone stood to their feet in respect. Then the audience sat down again to enjoy the music. The people showed their appreciation by clapping their hands.

When the choir stood up to sing the glorious Hallelujah Chorus, they sang with full voices "Hallelujah, hallelujah, hallelujah." To everyone's amazement, Queen Victoria rose to her feet in respect. It is true, that she was the most powerful Queen in the world at that time, but she felt that she must give honour to the

Lord, the King of Kings. Everyone else followed her example, and stood to their feet.

Ever since that day, when a choir sings the "Hallelujah Chorus," the listeners always rise to their feet, to give honour to the Lord, the King of Kings. For a similar reason, that is why we say at the end of the Lord's Prayer, "for thine is the kingdom, the power and the glory." It is a spoken chorus, or Doxology.

Prayer:

The Lord's Prayer.

Hymn:

Come and praise the Lord our King, Hallelujah. (C&P. 1. 21) or (J.P. 34)

Teachers' Note: (1) Most children love singing and music. (2) We may give honour to someone by singing as a choir. (3) The one to whom we owe the most honour is the Lord himself. This is why we call him, "The King of Kings". This is also why we repeat, "thine is the kingdom, the power and the glory," after the Lord's Prayer.

(c) Fiona's Birthday

Week 7   The Lord's Prayer

Praying and Good Deeds.

People grew to love the Lord's Prayer so much, because it was the actual words of Jesus himself. We all say it now, just like saying a poem. The danger in saying the prayer off by heart so often, is that we may say it, and not really mean it. However, we may turn our prayers into actions. When we pray it makes us love good deeds. There was once a poet called Samuel Taylor Coleridge. He wrote a poem called "He prayeth best." Here are a few lines ...

"He prayeth well who loveth well,
Both man, and bird and beast.
He prayeth best who loveth best
All things both great and small;
For the dear God who loveth us,
He made and loveth all."

Fiona was a happy little girl aged nine. She had heard that a special kind of hospital for children, called a "Hospice" had been built. She had been told that all the children in the Hospice were seriously ill. She also heard that the Hospice needed money.

She talked the matter over with her parents. Soon it would be her birthday, and usually she invited her school friends to her birthday party. She knew that they would be spending money to buy her birthday presents. Fiona also knew that she did not really need any of the presents. She thought of a wonderful idea. She would use her birthday to help the Hospice children.

Fiona sent a letter to her school friends, inviting them to her birthday party. The letter said, "No presents this time. Please, give donations to the Hospice instead." Many of the parents of the children who had been invited, thought that this was such a good idea, that they gave much more money than they would have spent on a present.

Fiona knew that doing it this way, she would be helping the sick children. She then arranged for a Disco to be held in the Church hall. She invited all the children from her class to attend the Disco. In this way she raised even more money for the Hospice.

Fiona was surprised that many other people also gave money. She found that she still received birthday cards from her friends. Imagine her surprise when she counted up all the money. It amounted to one hundred pounds. (£100)

However, she learned that when anyone collects money for a charity, that there are very strict rules. Parents, Head-teacher or Teacher must give permission. It is important that a receipt, or letter of thanks must be received back from the Hospice, for others to see.

Fiona wrote a letter, and sent the cheque for £100 to the Hospice. Soon she received a type-written letter back from the Hospice, thanking her, and her friends for the kind gift. All the children and their parents were happy because they felt that they had done a really good deed. *It is not enough to pray for sick children. Sometimes, we may turn our prayers into good deeds.*

Prayer:

> Father God, we thank you for our health.
> We pray for all sick children.
> We pray especially for children
> who lie seriously ill in a Hospice.
> Bless the kind doctors and nurses.
> Help us to turn our prayers
> into good deeds.   Amen.

Hymn:

> When I needed a neighbour. (C&P. 1. 65) or (J.P. 275).

Teachers' Note: (1). Saying prayers leads to thoughtfulness in children. (2). Children love to be involved in group good deeds. (The strictest procedures must be followed if money is being raised). (3). Fiona's is an example of a child's empathy with other children's suffering.

(a) Captain Scott Explorer

Robert Falcon Scott became the Leader of a party of experienced explorers from Britain. They made an attempt to reach the South Pole. When Scott and his party reached Melbourne (Australia) by sea, on the way to Antarctica, they received a telegram from another explorer. He was a Norwegian, named Roald Amundsen. The telegram informed them that Amundsen had also set up an expedition, and that he also was proceeding to Antarctica. This came as a complete surprise to everyone in Captain Scott's party.

Amundsen, intended to reach the South Pole first. Unexpectedly, the two expeditions turned into a kind of a race. Scott's party sailed in a whaling ship called the "Terra Nova". They reached snow-covered Ross Island early in 1911. Captain Scott's plan was to use motor tractors, ponies, and dogs to move food and the necessary equipment further along the the journey beforehand. (The seasons being the opposite to ours in the Southern hemisphere.) They did this before the terrible Winter weather conditions arrived in April. Captain Scott and his men had been doing a lot of scientific investigation and writing down results.

Amundsen's party sailed in a ship named the "Fram." Amundsen did not intend to do any scientific investigations. Instead, he had taken specially trained dogs, which could pull a light load. He wanted to reach the South Pole quickly, and return. Amundsen, forced his dogs to pull his four sledges over the snow, to the point where some of them became exhausted. He knew that the Winter weather and fierce blizzards could become so terrible, that his party must return their ship as soon possible.

Captain Scott, on the other hand, had heavy equipment. When he used his snow tractors to move baggage, the tractors either fell through the ice, or their engines froze up. The Siberian ponies were slow, but they carried the party a long way. The ponies later were shot, because they could not climb the Beardmore Glacier. They could not be left to die in the icy wilderness. Scott felt it was more humane to do this.

Scott sent the empty sledges back to the ship, pulled by the dogs. Moving onwards over the snow, Scott and the four remaining members of his party, Dr. Wilson, Lt. Evans, Captain Oates, and "Birdie Bowers" had to pull the sledge themselves. This made the men very tired.

Amundsen reached the South Pole, on the fourteenth December 1911. He stayed three days in a tent, and erected a Norwegian Flag there. Then he made his return dash by sledge to his ship. Scott's party took until the 16th January to reach the tent, and flag that Amundsen had left behind. Much to their disappointment, they realised that Amundsen had won the race to the South Pole, and that he gone home again.

They found letters addressed to them, which he had left behind. Scott's party erected a Union Jack to represent Great Britain. They now had to make the return journey of 1,300 kilometres across the ice, against blizzards, back to their base camp. They used a sail on the sledge, and the wind blew, helping them move more quickly. The snow blizzards became intense.

Everything seemed to go wrong for Scott's party. Evans fell ill and died. They all suffered from frostbite. They could only travel about ten miles each day. The cold was below 30 degrees centigrade. The tiny tent could not keep them warm. Captain Oates, badly frost-bitten, realised that he was dying. He bravely left the tent, and went out into a blizzard, and died alone in the snow, not wishing to be a hindrance to the party.

Scott's two companions, Bowers and Wilson were becoming weaker, as the weather worsened. Scott knew that they would never complete their return journey. They would be frozen to death. He wrote in his diary, "For God's sake, look after our people," meaning that the authorities in England should provide their wives and children with enough money to live on, since they were about to die.

These brave men died in their tent. They became an example of steadfast endurance to the world. Later, on the 12th November, 1912, their bodies and their diaries were found by a search party led by Atkinson, a surgeon. Scott's group had been only eleven miles from their base camp, when they died.

Some of the rocks collected by the explorers were two hundred million years old. They contained fossils proving that Antarctica had once been a hot tropical country. They also proved that Antarctica had once been joined to the continents of Africa and South America.

Prayer:

>Eternal Father, we respect the many brave people,
>who have lived before we were born.
>Especially, do we remember the great explorers
>such as Captain Scott and his expedition
>We remember men of courage like Amundsen.
>May we too live brave and cheerful lives.   Amen.

Hymn:

>He who would valiant be. (C&P. 1. 44) or (J.P. 80).

Teachers' Note: (1) The men of Captain Scott's expedition were scientists, looking for more knowledge about the earth. (2) All the explorers were brave men, including Amundsen. (3) The experience of disappointment at the South Pole, and the sad return journey, show us a good example of steadfast endurance under great dangers and difficulties.

(b) Joan of Arc

We must never forget that women are just as brave as men. Joan was a little French girl, who was born in Domremy, a village in Lorraine. She was a farmer's daughter who lived during the fifteenth century. Joan grew up to be a quiet religious girl, who loved to go to the village church. Sometimes she would sit alone in the church during the day.

However, she was also very strong, and worked in the fields, just like other peasant girls. She believed that the church bells had messages for her. She told people that she could hear voices talking to her in the ringing of the bells. The voices encouraged Joan to be faithful and good. Not only did she hear voices, but she also began to see visions of the Saints.

In those days, the English army had marched into France, and were defeating the French army. The people of France were very distressed to see the soldiers from England, marching through their villages. Joan heard the voices telling her that she was the Maid (girl) of Lorraine, who would rise up, and lead an army. She would save France by defeating the English army. The voices also told her that she would see a new king crowned at Rheims, who would become Charles VII of France.

When Joan was just sixteen, she told her father about the voices and her visions. She told him about what the voices had said. He laughed at her, because his daughter was only a farmer's girl. Joan returned to her work on the farm. Joan kept on hearing the voices. She went to see the Commander of a nearby town. He did not know what to think about this poor girl before him. However, the voices told Joan to dress up in a man's clothes. She rode miles on horseback, along with two young French soldiers, in order to meet the Dauphin, (Prince) who was to be the next King of France.

Joan convinced the French Prince that God had sent her to lead the army to victory. Joan was questioned by the Priests of the Church. Again, she told her story about the voices.

The army Commanders did not really believe her. However, they decided that because the French soldiers were so down-hearted, they could use Joan to inspire faith and new courage in the French army. They gave Joan a suit of armour, and dressed her in a scarlet and white overcoat. She rode a white horse. She was given an army of six thousand soldiers. A soldier carried a banner in front of Joan.

When the English army heard about Joan, they decided that she was a Witch. In 1428 Joan led her soldiers to Orleans, which was a walled city. It had been surrounded by the English army. She brought food, and the six thousand soldiers to help the people of Orleans fight the English army. The people in Orleans rang all the Church bells, and the English soldiers surrounding the city were afraid of the girl, whom they believed was a witch.

When the French army attacked the English army, Joan wore her suit of armour, and the standard-bearer carried her banner in front of her. Although she was wounded by an arrow in the shoulder, she led her army to victory. The English army ran in retreat. Everywhere, the French army won their battles. Eventually, the Dauphin, (Prince) was crowned King of France in Rheims Cathedral.

The voices had told Joan that she had only one year to save France. The year was now over. Joan asked to be allowed to return to her home village. The French Commanders were jealous of Joan's success. Now her voices warned Joan that she was in danger.

Joan was captured by a French Nobleman, the Duke of Burgundy. He sold her to the English for ten thousand livres. (one livre was worth about one franc). The English had Joan condemned to death. She was tied to a stake in the market place at Rouen, and burnt to death as a Witch, in the year 1430. So the brave Maid of Orleans who had saved her country ended her life's work.

Prayer:

> Lord, make us brave and true at all times.
> Give us courage, and kindness.
> Show us the ways of gentleness.
> We pray for any countries that may be at war.
> Grant them a lasting peace.
> May we have peace in our own hearts,
> and peace in our school.   Amen.

Hymn:

> I'm gonna lay down my sword and shield. (C&P. 2. 142)

Teachers' Notes: The point of this story is to realise that just as their are Patriots in the Bible, so there were good Christian people in other countries, who were also Patriots. A Patriot is someone who has a deep love for their country. They may also have a deep love for God and their religion.

(1) Joan was a simple, good, religious girl. (2) She lived at a cruel time, when wars were common. (3) Joan was burnt as a Witch. Witches do not exist, but there are some superstitious people, who still believe that they do.

(c) A Christian Slave

People are brave in different ways. A patient may be brave in hospital. A girl or boy may be brave in the school play-ground. A person may be very brave by apologising to someone else for wrong-doing.

In New Testament times there were thousands of slaves. To be a slave meant that a man or a woman, or a boy or a girl, were owned by a master, or a mistress. Slaves had no rights. They did not own anything. They could be bought or sold. The Law always took the side of the slave-master. Sometimes, a slave would have a kind master, and sometimes , a cruel master. Nevertheless, a slave had to obey. If slaves ran away, they might be killed if they were recaptured.

Onesimus, (pronounce "Onees-imus") was a slave in the town of Colossae. He was very fortunate slave, because his master, Philemon, was a Christian. Although Onesimus was better off than most slaves, he was unhappy about being a slave. He made a plan to escape. One dark evening Onesimus ran away. He travelled as far away from Colossae, as he could. Eventually, after travelling hundreds of miles, he reached the important city of Rome.

Paul, the Christian preacher, was growing old by this time. He had been put into prison, for his faith in Jesus. Onesimus visited Paul in prison. He brought Paul many of the things which he needed, such as food, or parchment and quill to write letters.

After a while, Onesimus told Paul his secret. He admitted that he was an escaped slave. Paul asked Onesimus what was the name of his master. Onesimus told him that his master's name was "Philemon, who lived in Colossae."

Paul smiled to himself, because he knew Philemon. Indeed, he had been able to teach him about Jesus, and Philemon had become a Christian. He knew that Christians met at Philemon's house and used it as a Church. After hearing Paul, Onesimus himself decided to become a Christian believer. He soon felt that he ought to return to his master, Philemon. This was a very brave action to take in those days, because he could have been dealt with very severely.

Paul, did not want Philemon to punish Onesimus for running away. He wrote a private letter to Philemon, asking him to receive Onesimus, not as a runaway slave, but as a Christian brother. Paul wrote that if Onesimus had done any damage, or owed Philemon any money, that he would pay it later. Onesimus said "Goodbye" to Paul, and took the letter. He travelled back the long journey to meet Philemon.

The New Testament does not say just what happened, when the runaway slave reached his master's house. Yet, we can imagine the scene. Onesimus in great fear, after his long journey, would knock the door of his master's house. The house-keeper, who was another slave, would open the door. She would run in to tell the master that Onesimus, was standing at the door, holding a letter in his hand.

Philemon would come out to meet Onesimus, and the slave would kneel before his master. Philemon, surprised, would read the letter from his friend Paul. Being a good Christian, he would receive Onesimus back into his house-hold, not just as a slave, but also as a Christian brother. Philemon would show forgiveness. They would shake hands. They would meet on the following Sunday at the Church. Onesimus would be introduced to all the other Christians. Everyone would be delighted that Onesimus had returned as a changed person, with a faith in Jesus.

Prayer:

> Lord, we thank you for everyone in the past,
> who worked to set people free.
> Father, we are happy that in our age,
> slavery has ceased.
> We are glad that in our school, we are free.
> Thank you for freedom for everyone.   Amen.

Hymn:

> Praise him, Praise him. (C&P. 1, 40) or (J.P. 202).

Teachers' Note: (1) Onesimus was a brave man because he dared to return to his previous master. (2) Paul was a brave man because he was willing to go to prison for his faith. (3) Philemon was a brave man because he held a Church in his own house, in the city of Rome.

(a) The Fortune Teller   *Week 9   Being Wise*

The old lady was wearing a red spotted head scarf at the fair ground. She was seated behind a small table, in her little tent. Outside the tent, there was a painted sign, which read "Fortune Teller." She asked everyone who came into her tent to sit down, one at a time at her table. Then, she asked them to put money into her hand. The people who came were all a little superstitious, and expected that she would tell them their fortune.

Most people did not believe in fortune tellers, but others were not so sure, so they paid the old lady, and waited to hear what she had to say. She always began, with the same question. "How wise are you?" Then she would hold up a card. It read:

2 Y'S U R, 2 Y'S U B. I C UR 2 Y'S 4 ME.

(It should read, "Too wise you are; too wise you be: I see you are too wise for me.")

She would look into a glass ball on the table. If you could read the card correctly, she would proceed to tell your fortune. If you could not read the words on the card, then she would pause for a little moment, as if she were thinking. Again, she would smile, and she would tell you, what she wanted to say anyway! For her it was all a bit of fun. Some people took the matter very seriously. One evening, when the fairground became quieter, the old fortune-teller, closed down her tent, folded up her little table, and went home to her cottage.

The three children next door, saw her coming, and they opened the gate for her.

"Can you really tell someone's fortune," they asked her. The old lady just laughed at the children. "No, of course, I cannot," she said, "but I can give you some ideas. It is really only entertainment. My glass ball was once an old paper weight. You see there are many people who are unsure of themselves, or perhaps, they are very unhappy for some reason. They do not tell me, but I know that they come for a word of encouragement. They would be wiser to attend Church, or read their Bible, or say a prayer".

She went on talking, "Just by looking at people, you can tell quite a lot about them. There is such a thing as body language. Looking at you three children, I can see that you have had a good dinner today. I can see that one of you fell as you were playing, and that an adult put a sticking plaster bandage over the graze on the skin. I can see that the two girls have been to the hair-dresser recently ,

I can see that you are well mannered, which means that you come from a good family. I can see that all you children love chocolate, and ice cream cones." She stopped talking, having run out of breath. "No, children, I can not make your future come true, by telling it."

"Come inside my little little cottage, and I will explain." The old lady gave each of the children a stick of plasticine. She asked them to squeeze the plasticine until it became soft and pliable. Then, she asked them to take the plasticine, and form a figure of themselves, showing what they might look like, when they had grown up. Each child used one little ball of plasticine as a head. Two pieces were used for arms, and another two pieces were rolled into legs. The children worked, until they had completed their figures.

The old lady looked at the three plasticine figures. "Now come," she said, "These three figures are like you children. Just as you have pressed a shape out of the plasticine, so you are able to mould yourself in different ways. You may try harder at your reading, your writing, your maths, or your sports. You are just like these plasticine figures, even your Teacher could not tell how you will turn out in the end."

The fortune-teller continued, "When you grow up, one of you may become a Nurse, and another may become a Police Lady, while the third, may turn out to be an aircraft Pilot. You never can tell! Whatever you do now, will affect the way you will turn out to be in the future." The three children remembered her words. "No-one knows what useful, and famous people, you may grow up to be. Work hard and do well!"

Prayer:

> Good Lord, we thank you that all our children,
> may have a happy future.
> Teach us all to do our best in the class room,
> and help us to mould our own wills,
> that we may become good learners.
> Help us to aim high, and try our best.   Amen.

Hymn:

> One more step along the world I go. (C&P. 1. 47) or (J. P. 188).

Teachers' Note: The Story Teller may add interest by making differing plastercine figures, as the story is being told. (1) All children have inner gifts, and strengths, which are yet to be developed. (2) Children may help themselves by learning to develop their own will-power. (3) The old fortune-teller talked honestly to the children.

(b) The Boy who loved Horses
Week 9   Being Wise

When Shahid came to England, from India, with his parents, he was seven years old. His Dad worked as a bus driver, and his Mum worked in a big super-market. Shahid had a problem. He was not as tall as the other children of his age. He hated to hear the older people saying, "Yes Shahid is very small, maybe he will grow taller as he gets older."

Shahid was a remarkable boy. First, he had a good brain. He found school, sometimes very easy, and other times, he had to study long hours to learn the English language. Yet, he soon caught up with the other children in the class. Shahid did grow taller, but he knew that he would never be as tall as the other young people, whom he knew.

The second remarkable fact about Shahid was that he loved horses. His home was in a housing estate. Behind his house, there were open fields, and farms. There were many cows, heifers, and bullocks in the fields. There were also some lambs and sheep. Shahid, saw the other cattle, in a matter of fact kind of way. However, when a horse, or several horses were grazing in the fields, his eyes used to light up with genuine pleasure.

The farmers noticed that Shahid had a very gentle manner, when he talked to a horse. Usually, the horses showed no fear. They came up to him, as he stood on the other side of the fence. They would allow him to stroke their long heads. He would pat them on the neck as if they were old friends. Strangely, he never wanted to be a jockey. He had watched the races on the television. He felt that sometimes jockeys were cruel to the racing horses, when they lashed them with their riding crops to make them go faster. Shahid had a gentler nature.

On a Saturday morning, he would go up to the farm, and help to sweep out the stables. It did not come as a surprise to anyone, when at sixteen years of age, Shahid, gained an "Apprenticeship" at the Riding Stables. This meant that for four years, he would learn all about horses, and how to groom them. He also learnt how to exercise them by galloping through the fields early in the morning. Sometimes the Apprentice Trainers would ride them along the seashore.

The Stable Owner, Mr. Oglethorpe, had chosen him out of many lads who had applied for the job, because he was small. This meant that he would not be too heavy to be a qualified Horse Trainer, when he grew to manhood. The second reason he was chosen, was because Shahid was intelligent. He paid attention to everything he had been told. Many young men and women make splendid stable-hands, but few are good enough to become real Trainers.

Among the many horses, there was one very expensive, chestnut-brown, racing horse, called "Prince Charming". Shahid was given the task of caring for this beautiful animal. Mr. Oglethorpe told him that he was responsible for the welfare of Prince Charming.

At all times, he had to keep a lock on the stable half-door. Before a big race, Shahid was expected to sleep on a camp bed in the stable, and guard his precious horse. This was not a problem, because the horse loved the young Apprentice in a mysterious way. Prince Charming learnt to recognise Shahid's low whistle.

It was a very happy time for both horse and stable-lad, until a terrible thing happened. One evening, a lorry came with a load of hay. The men unlocked the stable-door and loaded the hay into the double stable, as it would soon be dark. They were so busy in the other stable, that they did not notice the horse quietly walk through the door, and trot away into the darkness. Shahid, seeing that all the hay had been unloaded, now locked the stable door, and went off for his tea at the Big House.

One of the stable girls came rushing over to the house. "Someone has stolen Prince Charming. He is not in the stable," she shouted at the top of her voice. Shahid, laughed, and said, "Don't be silly, I locked the stable door half an hour ago!" They ran over, and looked over the locked stable half-door. The horse had gone. Mr. Oglethorpe came running over in the darkness. He was very angry!

"You have locked the door after the horse has escaped. You silly lad," he shouted. "He is out there somewhere in the hills, in the darkness."

Shahid was terribly frightened, and he felt that he had let everyone down. What could he do now. The valuable horse might get on a public road in the darkness and be run down by a car. What if Prince Charming had been killed?

When everyone was looking for lanterns, Shahid ran up the hill to the moor. He could not see anything. First, he prayed, "O Lord, help me to find Prince Charming." He put his fingers to his lips, and he gave a low shrill whistle, over and over again, in the darkness. He could hear Mr. Oglethorpe, panting out of breath beside him.

Almost immediately, he heard a horse make a whinny sound, and then a snort. Prince Charming came galloping up in the darkness, running past all the stablehands. All at once, the horse stopped at Shahid, rubbing his long nose in the lad's tee shirt, as if to say, "Here I am, and I'm frightened too". The lad quietly led the horse back in the dark to the stable yard, gently speaking to him.

Mr. Oglethorpe was so relieved that he forgot to be angry. He smiled, and said to Shahid, "It is no use locking the stable door, after the horse has bolted." The Apprentice never forgot those words. Shahid had grown to be a very wise lad. He always double-checked everything after that.

Because he was so wise about horses, Shahid was promoted to be an accredited Horse Trainer, and manager over the Riding Stables. He still never wanted to be a Jockey. When the Vet called once every week, he always asked Shahid about the sick horses, and the little long-legged foals. Shahid was glad that he had not grown tall, after all, because if he had, he would never have been able to become a Trainer , and ride the famous "Prince Charming".

Prayer:

> Father God, we thank you for smaller people,
> as well as for taller people.
> We thank you for those who are wise,
> and entrusted with the care of animals.
> Bless the work of Vets on the farms.
> If we get into in difficulty, teach us to pray.   Amen.

Hymn:

> When a knight won his spurs. (C&P. 1. 50)

Teachers' Note: (1) Shahid was small in stature. Many famous people have been small in stature, but large in understanding and sympathy. (2) Shahid made a mistake, because he was loading the hay in the evening darkness. Anyone can make a mistake. (3) Shahid had a special way with horses. Everyone has a personal gift.

(c) A Wise King

When King David died, he was buried in the city of Jerusalem. His son Solomon became king. Solomon wanted to be a very wise ruler of the land. One night, at Gibeon, God appeared to him in a dream. "You may ask for anything you want." said God to Solomon, "and I will give it to you."

Solomon replied, "Lord you were kind to my father, David, when he was king. Now you have made me king, in place of my father. More than anything else, I want a wise heart, so that I may be able to judge right from wrong, especially when people ask me to decide important matters."

God was very pleased at Solomon's reply. God said, "Because you have not asked for long life, or riches for yourself, but for wisdom, I will grant you what you have asked for. I will make you such a wise king, that no one will be equal to you in your life-time. More than that, I will give you what you have not asked for. I will also give you both riches and honour, beyond all other kings. If you obey me, like your father David, then I will give you a long happy life." Solomon woke up. He realised that he had been dreaming. He returned to the royal city of Jerusalem.

One day as Solomon sat in the seat of Judgment, two women arrived. They asked him to settle a quarrel. One of the women said, "This woman and I each had a baby. Her baby died during the night, so she took my baby when I was fast asleep. Then, she put her dead baby in my bed. When I woke up in the morning, I realised immediately, that the dead baby was not mine. She will not return my own living baby to me."

The second woman, argued back, "She is telling lies! The dead baby is her child, not mine. My baby is the living child."

Everyone wondered how king Solomon could ever find out which woman was the true mother of the living baby. Solomon looked at both women, then he called for a sword. Solomon gave an order, "Cut the living baby into two parts. Give one half to each mother." One woman became silent. The other woman, who obviously really loved the little baby, cried out. "O no! Do not kill the baby! Give the baby to her. I would rather give away my baby than let him be killed." Tears were running down her face.

Solomon immediately stopped the soldier using the sword. He said, "Do not harm the little child. Give the baby to the woman who wants to spare the baby's life. She is the real mother of the child! She really loves her baby." The little baby went home with its true mother, and that day, she was the happiest person in the world!

King Solomon was wise enough to know that mothers really love their own children. Everyone now knew that God had given wisdom to Solomon to rule the country wisely.

Prayer:

> We thank you for the gift of wisdom.
> We thank you for the love of mothers.
> Make us both wise and loving.
> Teach us not to be hasty in our judgment.
> Bless and protect all little children,
> by day and by night.   Amen.

Hymn:

> He's got the whole wide world in his hands. (J.P. 78)
> If using (C&P. 1.19). "He's got the tiny little baby in his hands,"
> may be added, and sung, to give relevance to the foregoing Assembly.

Teachers' Note: (1) Solomon asked God for an understanding heart. (2) God made Solomon wise in order to help others in his kingdom. (3) God loves all children in every land. (1 Kings Chapter 3)

(a) The Five Questions

The children in the school playground were asking each other riddles. Tracy asked them, "Why does the hen cross over the road?" When no-one could answer, Tracy laughed and said, "Because it wants to get to the other side." The children laughed at the simple answer. They knew that to get an answer, one must ask a question.

Rudyard Kipling was a famous Poet. He wrote a little verse about finding answers. It refers back to the time when people used to hire domestic servants, to do their work for them. Kipling writes:

> I kept six honest serving men,
> They taught me all I knew.
> Their names were, "Where, and What, and When;
> And Why and How and Who".

This poem means that if we want answers about anything, then we must begin with one of the questions, Where? or What? or When? or Why? or How? or Who?.

Liam was a lively boy, full of fun. Everyone liked him, because he was so thoughtful and kind. One afternoon Liam did not return to his class. The Teacher sent two of the older children to look for him around the school. Everyone had seen Liam at lunch time. The searchers looked around the school, but could not find the missing boy. Then they opened the door of the school boiler house, and looked inside. Usually, they were not allowed to open that door, because it was out of bounds. However, this was a special occasion. They looked inside, and found Liam lying unconscious against the wall, as if he were asleep. They tried to waken their friend, but he did not move.

They ran to their Teacher and told her, what they had seen. She rushed around to the boiler house, with the two older children. They saw that Liam was breathing very weakly, and that he could not wake up. The two older children remained with Liam, while the Teacher ran to telephone the ambulance, and the police.

The ambulance arrived within minutes and Liam was taken to the hospital. Liam was taken in to the Casualty Section. The problem was that the Doctors and Nurses did not know why Liam was ill. What had happened to Liam in the school boiler house? The police were asked to investigate.

The children were surprised to find that when the police car arrived, that it was two officers in ordinary clothes who came. They explained that they were Detectives, and that the hospital had asked them to come urgently, to find out what had happened. They had to report back immediately to the Doctors at the Casualty section.

The Detective spoke kindly to the children. "Do not be afraid of us. We are only here to ask questions." He began the questioning.

(1)   The first question was, "Who here saw Liam at lunch time?" All the children put up their hands.

(2)   The second question was, "Who was playing with Liam before he went missing?" Gerald said that he had been with Liam.

(3)   The third question was, "What was Liam doing when you saw him?" Gerald answered, " He had a tube of something in his pocket."

(4)   The fourth question was , "Where is Liam's coat now? He was not wearing it when he was found?" The two senior children said together, "Liam's coat is lying on the floor in the boilerhouse".

(5)   The fifth question was, "Who will take us to the boilerhouse?" The two senior children said, "We will show you, Sir."

The two Detectives and the two older children went to the back of the school, and looked in the boilerhouse. There in the corner was Liam's coat. It had been under Liam as he lay unconscious. The two Detectives searched the coat thoroughly, and there in one of the pockets, they found a long tube of glue. Immediately, one the Detectives pulled out his radio. He radioed the Casualty

Section at the hospital, and said, "Doctor, it seems that this lad has been sniffing glue."

The Doctors rushed to get Liam an oxygen mask, and the appropriate medicines. They knew that Liam would die, if they did not act very quickly. Liam was scarcely breathing. Now that the Doctors knew what the problem was, they worked quietly and quickly. The oxygen mask was placed over Liam's mouth, because his face had turned blue. The oxygen cylinder was turned on. Liam breathed the life saving oxygen into his lungs. After quite a long time, Liam's face became its usual colour, and he began to breathe normally again.

A few hours afterwards, Liam opened his eyes. The kind Nurse smiled, and said, "Now Liam you are going to get well." Liam went quietly to sleep again. Both his parents rushed to the hospital, and stood crying beside Liam's bed. Liam opened his eyes, and said, "Mum, I promise that I will never do such a foolish thing again."

It was six weeks before Liam was allowed back to school. He had nearly died, because of the foolish experiment he made. The Detectives also came back again that same week, to say, "Thank You" to the children, who could answer the five questions so clearly.

Neither Liam, nor any other child in the school was ever known to attempt to sniff anything out of a tube or a bottle again. They all knew that sniffing solvents could cause them to become unconscious, and they might die before anyone found them. Many of the children thought that they would like to become Detectives, or Doctors, or Nurses when they grew up, because these people were such helpful people.

Prayer:

> O God our Father, may we take care of our health.
> Enable us, never to do anything
> which would harm our bodies, or our minds.
> Teach us to be good examples,
> To other young people.
> We thank you for hospitals,
> Doctors and Nurses.   Amen.

Hymn:

> The ink is black, the page is white. (C&P. 1. 67)

Teachers' Notes: (1) Liam was a very happy boy, and normal in every way. (2) Liam made a foolish experiment that made him unconscious. It must have been a wrong action, because he was harming himself. (3) Liam's classmates answered the Detectives' five questions honestly and clearly, so they also had a part in saving Liam's life.

(b) The First British Martyr

In Bible times a martyr was a witness. A martyr was one who told the truth in a court about what he or she has seen happen. However, sometimes the meaning of a word changes over the passing of time. The word "Martyr" became used for anyone who was killed for telling the truth. There were many Christian martyrs who were killed for their faith in Jesus Christ. Whatever else a martyr did, he or she were always answering questions.

When the Roman army conquered Britain, they made splendid roads, and fortified towns across the country. Whenever you hear of an English town with the word "chester" in its name, you will know that the Romans once had a camp there, because "chester" means "a camp." (Latin, castra). eg; Manchester, Ribchester, Winchester, Chichester, Worcester, Colchester, and of course, Chester itself.

Alban was a Roman soldier, who's legion was stationed at Verulamium. One day he happened to meet a Christian Priest, who was escaping from the Roman authorities. As the two men talked together, the Priest explained that he had not broken any laws, but that he was in danger of being arrested, because of his faith in the Christian religion.

Alban was so interested in the Priest's conversation, that he brought him to his own house. He watched the Christian man very closely, and he could see that the Priest often knelt in private prayer to God. Alban asked the Priest many questions about the Christian faith. The Priest told Alban many of the stories about Jesus Christ.

Then Alban decided to follow a very brave plan. He made up his mind that he would hide this Christian Priest in his own house. For some time the Priest was safe from being arrested by the authorities.

After a while, some other people found out that Alban was hiding the wanted man in his home. Alban was reported to the Roman authorities. A band of soldiers was sent to his house to arrest the Priest. However, Alban continued to follow his plan to enable the Priest to escape. He exchanged clothes with the Priest. The Priest quietly escaped out the back door, when it was dark.

When the soldiers reached the house, Alban came to the front door, dressed up as a Priest. They arrested Alban, thinking that he was the runaway man. He was brought to the Roman Court, but the Judge soon realised that Alban was really a Roman soldier, and that the "wanted man" had escaped.

The Judge asked him many searching questions, and he gave clear honest answers. The Judge ordered Alban to offer sacrifice to the Roman gods. He refused to do so, because he had become a Christian. Alban was tortured in an attempt to make him change his mind. Even then, he refused to give up his faith in Jesus. The Judge ordered that Alban should be executed by being beheaded by the sword.

On the day of Alban's execution, the Roman soldier who was ordered to cut off Alban's head with his sword, refused to do so. This Roman soldier said, "Kill me in Alban's place, and allow Alban to go free, for he is a good man." The Judge was very angry, and ordered that both Alban and the soldier should be beheaded. Both brave soldiers were killed that day. They became, perhaps, the first Martyrs in England to die for their Christian faith.

No doubt, you will be wondering where Verulamium can be found on a map of England. The city name has been changed, and it is now named, St. Albans. If you go to visit the town, you will find that the beautiful cathedral built there has been also named after St. Alban

Prayer:

> Father God, we thank you for the bravery
> of Christian martyrs, such as St. Alban.
> We thank you for the brave people of every country,
> Who have been brave enough to give true answers.
> Make us good witnesses for our faith in God.
> Bless the good people of all religions.   Amen.

Hymn:

> I'm gonna lay down my sword and shield. (C&P. 2. 142)

Teachers' Notes: (1) Alban did a good deed when he opened up his home to the runaway Priest. (2) The Priest must have been a genuinely good person to have had such influence on Alban. (3) Alban answered the Judge's questions honestly because he had found faith in God.

(c) Greed for Riches   *Week 10   Answering Questions*

Here are two stories about people who were greedy for riches. The first story is about a rich young man who asked Jesus a question. The young man was so interested in his question, that he actually ran to meet Jesus. He showed real respect for Jesus, because he knelt down to ask his question. He said to Jesus, "Good Teacher, What shall I do to inherit eternal life?"

Jesus asked the young man a question in return. He said to him, "Why are you calling me good? No-one is good, except God alone. You know the Ten Commandments; Do not kill. Do not steal. Do not bear false testimony. Honour your father and your mother." The young man answered, "All these commandments I have kept since I was a boy."

Jesus looked at the earnest young man, and he loved him, because he could see that he was a sincere person. Yet he could see that there was one thing that the young man loved in his heart most of all. (His wealth). Jesus said to him, "You still lack one thing. Go and sell every thing you own, and give it to the poor people, and you will have treasure in heaven. Then, come and follow me."

The young man's face became very sad. He turned and went away home again, because he did not want to give up his great wealth. He was a very rich man. Jesus said, "It is easier for a camel to go through the eye of a needle, than for a rich man to enter the kingdom of God." Jesus meant that we must love God more than we love gold, silver, or any kind of riches.

The second story is an old legend about Midas, the King of Phry-gia. It is not to be found in the Bible, but it has a similar theme. Midas was a very greedy king, despite being very rich and powerful. He asked the gods that they would grant, that everything he touched, would turn to gold. They gave him his request.

Midas thought to himself, "Now I possess the power I have always wanted. I can touch stones and they will turn into lumps of gold, which I can sell for money. I shall be happy now, because I am the richest King on earth. Just think of it, I can touch anything, and it will change to gold." He laughed to himself.

Midas was beginning to feel very hungry, so he turned to a bowl of delicious fruit, which was on the table. As he lifted up a pear, it turned to gold in his hands, and when he took a bite, he nearly broke his front teeth. He threw it down and took an apple instead, but it also became shining gold. Now he was really angry, as he stretched out his hands, and grabbed a bunch of juicy black grapes. The grapes changed from black to a yellow golden colour. Midas now began to be afraid. If everything he touched were to become gold, then he would not be able to eat anything, and he would soon starve to death.

His lovely little Princess-daughter came running into the dining room. Midas loved his little girl very much indeed. He forgot about everything else, as he threw his arms around her to give her a father's hug. To his horror, the little girl changed from a living human being into a gold statute. Now Midas was terrified. He realised that he had been too greedy for gold. He had only himself to blame.

He pleaded with the gods to restore him to his past self. The gods ordered Midas to bathe in the river Pactolus. Strange to say, the river ever afterwards flowed over golden-coloured sands.

Now unlike the first story, this tale is only a legend, and it did not actually happen. The story of the rich young man, really happened and it is recorded both by Mark and Matthew. Can you see that both stories teach similar lessons. Loving gold, or silver, or possessions more than anything else is greed, and greed is wrong. Of course, we need to use money every day, to buy necessities, but it must never take first place in our hearts. We must always love God more than gold or money. How many things can you name that money cannot buy.

Prayer:

> Heavenly Father, help us to love you
> more than anything we may own.
> Inspire us to use our money.
> not only for ourselves,
> but also to help other children in need.
> Teach us the grace of giving,
> especially in our worship.   Amen.

Hymn:

> I saw a man from Galilee. (C&P. 2. 75)

Teachers' Note: (1). The Bible story teaches us that we may be greedy. Money is neither good nor bad, it was the "Loving of money" more than God, that made the rich young man wrong in the eyes of Jesus. (2) Midas was also greedy for gold. He had to learn the lesson that gold will not buy everything. (Health, appetite, peace of mind, faith, friendship, love of children, sleep, beauty, or personal skills.). (3) Money in itself is not bad; it can do much good in the world. Money may build schools, hospitals, churches, youth clubs, or wells in desert countries.

(a) The Fourth Finger   *Week 11   About Fear*

Our story begins in the time of Queen Victoria. There once were in the Scottish Highlands and islands many crofts. A croft is a small piece of land attached to a cottage. These little homes had thatched roofs made of straw or rushes. Often the cottages were near the sea. The people who lived in them were called "crofters". They usually lived together in a group of cottages.

Ian was a crofter's son, and his father and mother loved him dearly. His mother taught him many things. When Ian was very small, and just learning to walk and talk, she taught him the words of the twenty-third Psalm. This is the Psalm which begins, "The Lord is my shepherd, I shall not want." Mother had a deep faith in God.

She taught Ian to hold his left hand flat, and to point to his thumb, and say, "The". Then Ian would point to the second finger and say "Lord". He would point to his third finger and say "is". When he came to his fourth finger, his mother would always say, hold your fourth finger tight, and say "my". Then he would point to his fifth finger, which was the little finger, and say, "Shepherd".

Ian grew up into a strong boy, of seven years old. He never forgot the peculiar way he was taught to repeat the first verse of the Psalm. He never forgot to hold his fourth finger, when he said "MY shepherd". Mother had told him, that if ever he was afraid, he was to remember that the Lord was like a shepherd who takes care of us all.

Of course, Ian knew what being a shepherd meant. His father had been a shepherd all his life. He cared for his sheep. He was kept busy at lambing time. They owned a very clever Collie sheep dog, by the name of "Fly." Although Ian was only seven, he wanted to be a shepherd like his father.

The Winter winds blew hard that year, bringing heavy falls of snow on the mountain side. The sheep knew how to huddle together. Sometimes the snow would cover them entirely, and they would be hidden from view under the snow. Ian looked out of his warm home, with its peat fire blazing in the hearth. His father had told him that one of the sheep had given birth to a very early lamb, just before the snow had fallen.

Ian worried about the lamb becoming cold, and dying before they could find it again. He decided to put on his coat, and wrap a scarf around his head. He took his father's crook, which was a rather long walking stick, with a hook on the top of it. He climbed the side of the hill, and crossed the stream. He knew how to prod the crook into the snow to find the sheep lying underneath.

It became very dark, and in the gloom, Ian suddenly found a flock of sheep, huddled under the snow. He cleared some of the snow away, and there they were lying underneath. His heart gladdened as he saw the mother ewe, and the tiny lamb. The snow began to fall heavily again. Ian realised that he could not return in the darkness. He was a wise lad, and did not panic. Instead, in the darkness, he cuddled down in the snow, surrounded by the other sheep. Soon they were all asleep, and buried by the snow.

Ian's parents were very worried when Ian did not return. They realised that they would have to wait until morning. They wondered whether Ian might be found dead on the mountain-side at day-break. Father awoke very early next day, and called "Fly". He said to the dog, "Go girl, and find Ian". The dog barked loudly as if he understood, and went racing up the hill, with Dad following his experienced sheep-dog. The dog was trying to find the scent of living beings. Fly was also looking for the hole in the snow which sheep make by the warmth of their breath coming up from underneath.

At last she found the hole, and she pushed her nose into it. The sheep and Ian were lying fast asleep underneath the snow. Ian's father came panting up the hill. "Good girl" he said, "You have found them!" Dad cleared away the snow, and there he saw Ian cuddling the tiny lamb, and sleeping against the warm wool of the sheep.

He looked at his son, and he could see that Ian was holding the fourth finger of his left hand, as if to say in his sleep, "The Lord is MY shepherd, I am not afraid." Ian awoke, and was happy to see his father and Fly. The wise dog gave Ian a lick, and wagged her tail. Ian carefully carried the little lamb down the mountain on his shoulder. Father and Fly followed until they reached the crofter's cottage. They were all safe and well again.

They each had a hot meal (including Fly) sitting beside the fire. Mother opened the family Bible, and she read the first verse of the twenty-third Psalm again. "The Lord is my shepherd, I shall not want." She smiled at Ian because she knew just why he was holding his fourth finger.

Prayer:

> Lord, you are our shepherd
> and we are your sheep.
> May we not wander away on false paths.
> Guard us all, and guide us,
> in our daily everyday lives.
> Grant us the assurance that
> God takes care of each one of us,
> now and always.   Amen.

Hymn:

> The Lord's my shepherd. (C&P. 1. 56) or (J.P. 243).

Teachers' Note: (1) Ian's mother loved the poetry of the Bible, and she taught Ian to remember it. (2) Ian found and understood personal meaning in the Shepherd Psalm, when he held his fourth finger at the word "My". (3) Jesus, our Lord, cares for each one of us. He once said, "I am the Good Shepherd".

(b) The Two Teeth   *Week 11   About Fear*

Patricia was a lovely Welsh girl who lived in a beautiful valley in Wales. Being eight years old, she was usually very happy. Although, if you could have read Patricia's thoughts, you would have known that Patricia had one great secret fear, about which she had never told anyone. Her parents did not even know. Patricia was afraid of going to the dentist.

She had lovely shiny white teeth, until one day, she looked into the mirror, and she saw that she had a tooth with a black hole in it. The decayed tooth was a big tooth at the back of her mouth. To make things worse, she found that another front tooth was becoming wobbly. Patricia was really scared now. She showed the bad tooth to her mother. Mother said that she would have to go to the dentist, and let him deal with it. She didn't tell her mother about the wobbly tooth.

That night when Patricia went to bed, she began to worry. The dentist might hurt her, she thought. He would probably be an old fellow, who didn't like children. He might stick needles in her gums and make her cry. Patricia really was terrified at the very thought of going to visit the dentist. In the end, she had to go, since her mother had made the appointment.

She arrived at the dentist's waiting room, and the receptionist wrote her name down in the register. There were about six people waiting to see the dentist, and none of them seemed to be bothered or worried in any way. They either sat and talked together, or read the glossy magazines which had been provided to pass the time.

Then a dental nurse came out, dressed in a white coat. She was young, and smiled at everyone. Patricia thought that she looked beautiful and kind. She took Patricia through the door, into the dentist's clinic. Patricia was most surprised when she saw the dentist. It was not an old man, but another young lady, whose parents had originally come from India.

The lady dentist asked Patricia to sit on a chair, which could be reclined with a press of a button. The dentist looked inside Patricia's mouth, using a tiny battery torch. "Oh" she said, " Patricia, you have one bad tooth at the back, I must drill a little hole in it, and then fill it." Patricia was really terrified. The dentist kept talking to Patricia, asking her, "Are you sure that you are comfortable now?"

She put a long sharp instrument into Patricia's mouth, and touched her gum with it. It did feel rather strange, but it was not really painful. "Now, just wait for five minutes," the dentist said. It was really strange, because when Patricia touched her gum with her tongue, she could not feel anything. The dentist, then used another electric instrument on her tooth. She could feel the grinding sensation, but it was not sore in the least.

The dentist filled her tooth, with a tiny amount of what looked like soft white cement. She polished all her teeth with an electric brush. Then the dentist said, "That will be all just now. Please, come back in six months, and we will check your teeth again." Patricia could not believe that it was all over. She realised that she had been worried and fearful for nothing. She knew now that there was no need to worry about going to visit the dentist.

As she was going out through the door, led by the dental nurse, she remembered about her loose tooth in the front of her mouth. Patricia turned back to the dentist, and said to her, "You forgot to pull out my loose tooth." The lady dentist smiled at Patricia, and replied, "Oh no, I did not forget anything. If I pulled out that loose tooth, then you might lose ten pence."

"You tell your mother what I said. You will find that tooth will fall out one day by itself. When it falls out, put it under your pillow, tell your Mum or Dad, and you might find ten pence beside it when you wake up in the morning. On the other hand, you might find nothing! If it works, it usually only works for the first tooth. It is worth a try. The secret is to tell your parents."

Patricia thought how silly she had been to be afraid of the dentist. She was not superstitious, and she didn't believe in the Tooth Fairy story. Yet she told her Mum and Dad about what the dentist had said, about the loose tooth. Dad winked at Mum. Next week Patricia's loose tooth fell out, and she put it below her pillow, and told her parents. Sure enough, next morning, when she awoke, there was a shiny ten-pence coin under her pillow. The dentist was right, it only happened once!

Prayer:

> Good Lord, save us from our secret fears.
> Teach us to bring our worries to God in prayer.
> We thank you for doctors, dentists, and nurses,
> who work to bring us healing and health.
> We pray for all sick children in hospitals.
> Bless us this day, and may we do our best.   Amen.

Hymn:

> Kum ba yah, my Lord, Kum ba yah. (C&P. 1. 68) or (J.P. 149)

Teachers' Note: (1) Patricia's fear was a fear of the unknown. She was completely wrong about the dentist as a person. (2) Both the dentist and the nurse happened to be ladies. That was a surprise. (3) Tell the children, honestly that there is not such a thing as a "Tooth Fairy." It is usually a parent who puts the money under the pillow, because the child is dearly loved.

(c) The Man without Fear   *Week 11   About Fear*

John the Baptist by the river Jordan

There was once a fierce looking preacher in New Testament times, who preached near the river Jordan. The people called him "John the Baptist" because he baptised people in the river, as a sign that they had been changed from their evil ways. He used water as a sign that their lives had been washed clean from wrong-doing.

John used to quote Isaiah the prophet, and say that he was, "The voice of one crying in the wilderness, "Prepare the way of the Lord." John wore rough clothing, made from camel's hair. He wore a leather belt around his waist. He fed on locusts and wild honey, which he found in the countryside.

John's preaching drew large crowds of people from the city of Jerusalem. He was fearless. When the religious leaders came to be baptised, he rebuked them, calling them, "vipers" (snakes), because they only pretended to be good. When the Tax Collectors came, John warned them that they must stop taking more tax than was really due, and putting the extra money in their own pockets. John declared that this practice was stealing.

He even rebuked king Herod. John said that because the King had rejected his wife, and taken another Queen, that the lady he had chosen, was not really his wife. Herodias, the new Queen, was very angry. She hated John, for saying such things.

When Roman soldiers came, John told them that they must not be violent to any person. They were not to accuse anyone falsely, and they must be content with their wages. People were so impressed by this fearless preacher, that they wondered whether he might be the promised Christ (Messiah) . John always told his listeners, "I am not the Christ. Someone is coming after me, who is more powerful than I am. I am not worthy to undo the thongs on his sandals."

One day, Jesus came to the river Jordan to be baptised by John. However, John stopped Jesus, saying, " This should be the other way round. I need to be baptised by you, why are you coming to me?" Jesus said, "John for the sake of setting an example, to others, allow this to happen!" So John baptised Jesus in the river.

A strange thing happened. The moment John baptised him, and Jesus came up out of the water, the Spirit of God, in the shape of a dove appeared. The dove settled on the head of Jesus. A voice was heard, saying, "This is my beloved son in whom I am well pleased." This appearance of the dove meant that God's Spirit was with Jesus in a very special manner. Nowadays, the symbol of the dove is used as the symbol of peace.

John the Baptist in prison

Sometime later, Herod the evil King, put John into prison. John was a little confused about why God had allowed him to be put into prison. He even wondered whether Jesus was the true Messiah, or not. He sent a message to Jesus, asking him, "Are you the Messiah who was to come, or should we look for someone else?"

Jesus sent back a reply to John. "Go back to John and tell him everything you see and hear. Blind people are being cured and made to see again. Lame people are being healed and can walk again. Lepers are being cured. Deaf people can hear again. Poor people have the gospel preached to them."

Then Jesus turned to the crowd, and he explained what he really thought of John the Baptist. He said, "There has not been anyone born greater than John the Baptist."

Herodius the Queen, had a beautiful daughter, who was an excellent dancer. At a feast, the girl danced before King Herod. The King was so pleased with the young dancer, that he said in rash words, "Ask of me anything, and I will give it to you, even to half my kingdom." The daughter ran to her mother, Herodias, and asked her, what present she should ask from the King. Her mother replied, "Ask for the head of John the Baptist on a plate."

King Herod was trapped by his own words. His friends had heard him make the promise to the dancing girl. Therefore, he had to send soldiers to the prison to behead John the Baptist. The soldiers killed John. They brought his head on a plate, and presented it to the daughter, who in turn gave the horrible present to her mother. In this way, Herodias had gained her revenge on John for his condemnation of her marriage to the King. This was the sad end to the life of the fearless man of God, John the Baptist. Jesus kept on preaching the good news, and healing sick people, until he also was killed.

Prayer:

> Heavenly Father, we thank you
> for John the Baptist.
> We are glad that he was not afraid,
> to preach God's message of the Gospel.
> We are glad that you showed your pleasure,
> at the Baptism of Jesus, by sending the dove,
> and by anointing him with the Holy Spirit.
> Make us all kinder and more helpful pupils.   Amen.

Hymn:

> Go tell it on the mountain. (C&P. 1. 24) or (J.P. 65).

Teachers' Note: The moral in this story is that sometimes good people have to suffer for the Lord. (1) John the Baptist was like a herald who went ahead to announce to the people, that the King was coming behind him. This is what he meant by calling himself, "a voice crying in the wilderness". (2) Jesus was without sin. The reason that he was baptised was to set people a good example. (3) Being baptised means that we have been made members of Christ's Church, and congregation, even though we may be young.

(a) Fred's Happy Christmas   *Week 12   Toward Christmas*

Old Fred lived under the railway arches in London. Really, it would be more true to say, that old Fred lived in a large cardboard box under the railway arches. He had no home of his own. Fred had given up hope long ago of having a home.

During the Summer time, when the nights were warmer, Fred liked to sleep on a bench in the public park. The policemen on their night beat, did not give him any trouble. Usually, in the darkness, an officer would shine a torch on his face, and ask him, if he were all right.

Then, the police officer would move on his beat. There were many more tramps such as old Fred. There were also young people who had left home to find work in the big city. When they could not find work, they could not pay for proper lodgings, so they either had to find a Hostel, or sleep rough.

With Fred it was different. He had become used to sleeping rough, under the railway arches. At one time, he had a happy home in Glasgow. Sadly, his wife died early in their marriage. Fred was broken hearted. He had to give up his home, and he came to England, to find a job as a labourer on the farms. Then he just drifted from one job to the next, until finally, he ended up in London. His health was not good and he was often wheezing and coughing. He did not care what happened to him now.

Often, the Officers of the Salvation army visited him as he slept under the arches. Tonight, they brought him a cup of warm tea, and a some sandwiches. On other occasions, Fred would make his way along to the mobile soup kitchen, which was a large motor van. He knew that he could always get a bowl of soup, about eleven o'clock at night.

Now it was Christmas week, and as he walked painfully along the dark streets, he smiled to himself. This was the one week in the year, when a tramp could stay at the Hostel, free of charge, and get hot meals made for him. He knew that he would have a clean warm bed for seven days. The Hostel workers were mostly kind people attached to a church, or some charity, who tried to help tramps like himself, who were "down and out."

Old Fred lay in the warm Hostel bed. He remembered his childhood and how he had attended a Glasgow school. He had hoped to become a professional footballer, but he was never good enough at the game, to be signed up by a professional team.

Then he brightened up again, because tomorrow was Christmas day. He loved Christmas because it reminded him of the happy times they had at home. His mother used to make him turkey and Christmas pudding. He remembered also her plum puddings. They were delicious! His father worked at John Brown's shipyard. Dad always bought or made his son Fred, at least one toy for Christmas.

Fred remembered, that one year he had said to his Dad, "Make me a boat for Christmas, one like the 'five three, four'." (When ships are being built, they do not have a name, but rather a number. Number five, three, four, was the work-number used by the ship-builders, for the largest ship in the world, which at that time, was being built on the river Clyde. We all now know of her as the ocean going liner, "Queen Mary."

This was the passenger liner that won an award called the "Blue Ribbon" for the fastest crossing of the Atlantic Ocean. Old Fred remembered that his Dad wakened him on Christmas morning, and gave him, a model of the "Queen Mary" Fred sailed it in the bath, and on the park pond. Fred was happy with the memories of his childhood, and he fell asleep, dreaming of the "five, three, four,".

Next day was Christmas! The kind people at the Hostel served all the tramps, and homeless people with the best of food. At three o'clock in the afternoon, they all sat down to the most wonderful Christmas turkey-dinner they ever had seen. All sorts of goodies were on the table, and Fred finished off his dinner with mince pies, and a cup of hot tea. Fred thought to himself, "I will have to go back to sleeping under the arches next week. How awful!" He shivered at the thought. The icy cold wind whistled across the river Thames.

Before he went to sleep that night, Fred opened a Bible which was nearby. He could not get the numbers "five, three, four," out of his head. He turned to St. Luke's Gospel, chapter five, and he read verses three and four.

It read, *Jesus embarked on one of the boats belonging to Simon, and asked him to put out a little from the shore. Then he sat down, and taught the people from the boat. When he had finished speaking, Jesus said to Simon, "Put out into deep water, and let the nets down for a catch."*

He thought to himself, "St. Luke chapter five, verses three and four, is about Jesus being in a boat, and sailing out into the deep sea. It is just like the the other five, three, four I once knew about, when I was a boy. The "Queen Mary" was a bonnie ship, when she sailed out into the deep water." Old Fred smiled, and fell fast asleep, dreaming of his childhood. This Christmas day had been the best he had known for a long time.

Christmas is not just about getting toys. It is a time to be with people, and a time to share with those who love and care for us. Fred was not able to be with his family, but he was still able to spend Christmas with people, who showed him love and care.

Prayer:

> Father God, we thank you for Christmas time.
> We pray for the many homeless people,
> who have lost all hope, and who need our charity.
> May the story of the first Christmas,
> bring joy and faith into their hearts.
> Bless the good people who provide for the poor.   Amen.

Hymn:

When the Winter day is dying. (C&P. 2. 118)

Teachers' Note: (1) The reason for this story is to emphasise that Christmas is a social event connected with the poor and homeless. (There was no room in the Inn for Mary and Joseph, or their baby Jesus). We ought to thank God for our homes. (2) There are many good people who care for homeless people all the year round. (3) Fred's Christmas was a very happy one because it reminded him of his own childhood home.

(b) St. Nicholas and the Three Bags   *Week 12   Toward Christmas*

Do you know where the name, "Santa Claus" came from?

The assembly begins with a game of "Chinese Whispers." A line of children stretches across the assembly hall. In order to illustrate how messages get changed, as they are being told, the child at the end of the line, is given a message in whispers, to pass to the next child. The second child whispers the message to the third child, this continues, until the garbled message reaches the child at the end of the line. The first message is then compared with the last message, to reveal how words are changed in their telling.

The story of Santa Claus goes far back to the fourth century to the legend of St. Nicholas. There was once a Bishop of Myra, by the name of Nicholas. After he died, many stories were told about this good man. Many people told stories to pass on information to their younger people. These stories often changed as they were being told.

Because there was no cinema or television in those days, painters were very popular. They could paint pictures of famous people, or scenes from the Bible, so that anyone who could not read, could at least enjoy looking at a picture. The paintings showing St. Nicholas, often depict him wearing Bishop's robes, and three money bags are included in the pictures.

The reason for including the three money bags, comes from an old story. When Nicholas lived in the town of Myra, he knew of a very poor family who lived nearby. The man had three beautiful daughters. When each daughter wanted to be married, and a suitable young man was willing to marry one of them, there was always a problem. The father being only a poor man, could not afford to give a dowry with his daughter in the proposed marriage. It was the usual custom to provide a dowry, as a gift to the young husband, who would be marrying, and caring for the daughter all his life. (A dowry could be a gift of money, or cows, or sheep, or something valuable).

Nicholas was a good-hearted person, so when the poor man's eldest daughter was about to be married, in order to save them from hunger, he went out when it was night. He threw a bag of gold coins down the chimney of the poor man's house, where it fell on the daughter's shoes and stockings, which were warming beside the fire. The eldest daughter was able to marry after all.

Nicholas did a similar kind deed, when the second daughter was about to be married. Again, he threw a bag of gold coins down the chimney on the second daughter's shoes and stockings, which were warming beside the fire. So she also had a marriage dowry to bring to her husband. Nicholas never told anyone, that he himself was the kind-hearted giver.

When the time arrived for the poor man's third daughter to be married, again Nicholas went out when it was night, and once more, he threw a bag of gold coins down the chimney. This time, the poor father was hiding in the darkness. He saw that the kind giver was Nicholas. The poor man thanked Nicholas with all his heart. However, Nicholas made the father promise that he would never tell anyone what he knew.

This may be the reason why in some countries, especially Holland, children receive presents on the evening of the 5th. December, which is the evening before St. Nicholas Day. (6th). Sometimes their parents hide presents about the house, and the children have to search to find them.

When settlers from Holland went to America, they carried the story of St. Nicholas with them. They shortened his title from St. Nicholas to "Sinta Class." After a time the Americans began to use the name, "Santa Claus".

In Britain, "Santa Claus" has slowly become accepted as his proper name. He is no longer depicted dressed in a Bishop's robes, wearing a mitre on his head. Now he is shown as a happy man, with a beard, dressed in red clothing, wearing a red hat, and black boots. Santa, in Britain, always carries a bag full of presents. We are told by some people that he travels at night in a sleigh, pulled by eight reindeers. He is said, to always visit the children with presents on Christmas eve, the evening before the 25th. December.

The whole meaning of the Santa Claus legend is that of "Giving," rather than that of "Getting." We may grow away from believing in the old legend, but we must never grow away from its meaning. Jesus said, "It is better to give than to receive." Have you prepared your gifts, ready to give to someone this Christmas?

Prayer:

> Lord God, we thank you for Christmas time
> Help us to understand its deep meaning.
> It is more blessed to give, than to receive.
> We praise you for the true story,
> of the baby Jesus, born in a manger.

Give us all a happy Christmas,
through Jesus Christ our Lord.   Amen.

Hymn:

The Virgin Mary had a baby boy. (C&P. 2. 121) or (J.P. 251).

Teachers' Note: (1) Legends are old stories, only partly true, yet they teach us a good moral. (To be generous instead of being greedy). (2) Nicholas helped poor people. All children will out-grow the story of, "presents coming down the chimney". The Legend explains, perhaps, where the idea came from. (3) Christmas is about God giving us Jesus, as a baby being born in a manger. This is a true story, and not a legend.

(c) The First Christmas   *Week 12   Towards Christmas*

This assembly is best told as a, "piece of drama," spoken by the Teacher, acting as the old shepherd, who is telling the story of what happened to him, (or her), as a young person.

"Let me tell you of the events, which I saw when I was a young man. Allow me to tell you, as I still remember it so vividly in my mind. "I was a shepherd boy, and my name is Philip. I lived quite near the little town of Bethlehem, here in Judea. Some strange happenings were taking place in our district. Let me tell you about them in my own words! Now, I never had the opportunity to go to school, so I cannot read or write. You will have to bear with me, as I tell you my tale. As I said, I am not a scholar, but I do my best to tell you, anyway!

We were out in the fields, in the hill country, watching over our flocks of sheep. While the rest of us were asleep at night, at least two of our company, usually have to remain awake, in case any wolves come, to kill the sheep. We kept a good fire going, because the moving flames scare wild animals away. One night, as most of us were asleep, a sound like a choir singing in the dark skies was heard.

Suddenly, there was a bright, almost blinding light, and everyone of us were wakened. We were badly frightened. Then, a strange figure was seen in the distance. He was like a man with wings, hovering in the dark sky The figure spoke out clearly, "None of you need be frightened. I bring good news. Today, in David's town, a Saviour baby has been born. He is to be called the "Christ". If you go to visit him, look for this sign. The baby will be lying in a cows' manger, wrapped up in swaddling cloths.

Just at that very moment, it was as if a choir in the sky appeared over us. The heavenly choir sang, "Glory to God in the highest, and on earth, peace to mankind." I have never heard such singing before. It was marvellous! Then the light darkened, and it became night again. Honestly it really happened!

Next morning, a few of our shepherds were left to guard the sheep, while the rest of us, went down to Bethlehem. We wanted to see if there were any truth in what the the heavenly choir had told us. We found Joseph and Mary in a stable, and there, sure enough, there was the baby lying in a manger. We told them of the heavenly choir, and what they had been singing about.

Joseph thanked us. Mary smiled, but she did not say much. It was as if she was keeping her thoughts about her baby to herself. My shepherd friends, and I, went back to our sheep, but we felt that we ought to sing a hymn to the Lord, as we climbed back up the hill again.

It was just around that time, that Matthew, another member of our friends' group arrived, and he gave us, an even more curious report. He told us that 'Wise men from the East', had arrived. He said that they looked just like merchants, riding on camels. Apparently, the Wise Men had travelled hundreds of miles.

These people, from a distant land, had been used to studying the stars. They had discovered a specially bright star in the sky, and they determined to track its course. At the same time, they were convinced that this special star had appeared, because a royal baby had been born. This baby was to be the future King of the Jews.

These 'wise men' had travelled far, and naturally called to visit Herod's royal palace. They asked at the palace whether a royal baby had been born there, because they had gifts for the child. The wise men said that a special star had been seen in the sky, foretelling the birth of a great king. They explained how they had followed the star.

Herod the King, listened to the wise men, and he made up his mind to kill the new-born baby. He asked the visitors to find the baby, and to bring a report back to him. These travellers left King Herod, and continued their search. All the time they were following the bright star.

Eventually, the star stopped over a stable in Bethlehem. The wise men had brought three gifts for the baby. They went inside the stable. They met Joseph and Mary. Then, they reverently knelt before the baby Jesus, and worshipped him. They gave the baby presents of gold, incense, and myrrh, (a kind of ointment). They bowed again, and left the baby with his parents.

God had warned the wise men in a dream, that they were not to report back to King Herod, but to go home by another way. It was also by means of yet another dream that the angel of the Lord warned Joseph, that King Herod would try to kill the baby. The angel had said, "Take the baby and his mother, and escape into Egypt. Stay there until I tell you that it is safe to return". When it became dark,

Joseph and Mary escaped carrying their baby with them. They are sure to remain in Egypt, until King Herod had died."

Now as sure as my name is, "Philip the shepherd", everything I have told you is true! I didn't understand just what was happening. After all, I'm not a scholar. When I looked at the baby Jesus myself, that day, the little infant smiled back at me, and I felt blessed all over. It was as if God had touched me. That baby was someone very special. I tell you it was all a mystery!

Prayer:

Heavenly Father, we praise you for the angel song.
We thank you for the good news
about the birth of Jesus, our Lord and Saviour.
Like the Wise Men, we also rejoice.
May the angel song of peace on earth,
bring happiness to all children around the world.   Amen.

Hymn:

As I went riding by, I saw a star in the sky. (C&P. 2. 120)
or See him lying on a bed of straw. (J.P. 214)

Teachers' Note: (1) The Shepherds represent the ordinary people of those days. (2) The wise men represent the better educated kind of person. The point is that both types of people worshipped Jesus. (3) The birth of Jesus shows just how poor he really was. The choral song in the dark sky means that God wants to bring peace on earth to all kinds of people.

The whole lesson could be easily adapted as a childrens' mime, with children dressed as Shepherds, Wise men, and King Herod's Soldiers. The mime could be interspersed with carols. One, or two adults could read Philip and Matthew's accounts, and ad lib in parts of the narrative, in order to heighten interest.

Spring Term

(a) The Big Snowman

There were two Primary schools on the same side of the road. The schools were separated by a large field, which both schools used as a playing field. When the Winter came, and the snow fell on the field, the children from one school, would throw snowballs at the children from the other school. Many of the Infant children, were frightened by the rough play of the older children. The Christmas holidays were past, and the children were back again at school.

It was the second week of the New Year, and sure enough, one cold evening, the snow flakes began to fall from the sky, just like large goose feathers. The children became excited at home, as they looked out of their windows. They all wanted to get outside to enjoy the snow, but it was becoming dark. They hoped that the snow would not be washed away by the rain in the morning, when they had to go to to school. Many of them decided to try to get to school early. They loved to have extra time to play in the snow.

Next morning, when the children woke up, and looked out side, they saw that the snow had fallen all through the night. There was not a trace of rain, so the snow was dry and crisp. The snow drifts near walls and buildings were nearly a half-metre deep! Cars were having difficulty driving on the snowy roads. The children rushed their breakfasts, and put on their warm coats, hats, and gloves. They urged their parents, and friends to get them to their school playing-field as early as possible.

Ben was a big boy, ten years of age. He had a little sister, called "Sarah" who was six years of age. They trudged through the deep snow to their school. More children arrived at the second school on the other side of the playing field. The older children from both schools began to throw snowballs at each other. The big playing field looked more like a battle-field, with two armies fighting each other. The younger children were terrified.

As the whistle was blown in the school yard, it could be seen that some of the younger children had begun to make a number of little snowmen, here and there. Ben had said to Sarah on the way to school, "Let us get all the children from both schools together. During the dinner hour, we will build the biggest snowman anyone has ever seen." Ben asked the older boys and girls in both schools to join together, to help the younger children to build a really big snowman. The older children from both schools agreed to meet on the playing field during the dinner hour.

The Head-teachers in both schools gave permission for all the school children to use the school playing field, for this united endeavour. The older children had to promise to take care of the younger ones.

At dinner time, there were more than two hundred excited boys and girls gathered together in the snow. The older boys marked out a ring on the ground as a base for the snowman. Everyone began to collect snow in their hands, in order to pile it higher and higher, to make the snow man. Their fingers were very cold indeed. Then, Ben had a bright idea. We all have plastic clip boards in the school. Let us ask permission from our teachers, to use our clip boards as little shovels. We can dry them off afterwards. So now the children from both schools could really work fast. Even the little ones could collect snow on their clip board.

In half an hour, the children from both schools working together, built the tallest snowman they had ever seen. Next they rolled a large snowball, for the snowman's head. The big boys lifted the large snowball on top of the snowman's shoulders. Some children used stones to make the snowman's eyes, and nose; more stones were used as buttons down the front of his imaginary coat. Someone shouted, "He hasn't got a mouth". Ben took a banana from his lunch box, and pushed it into the snowman's face, and it just looked like a large smiling yellow mouth Some of the year four children brought an old hat for his head, and a scarf, to put round the snowman's neck, from the lost property box. At last the snowman was completed. He looked like a real snowman! They were amazed because he appeared to be huge.

None of the children were aware of it, but the teachers had been watching through the school windows, and they were using the telephone to speak to the teachers in the school across the playing field. Soon, they had telephoned the local newspaper, and told the Editor what was happening. The newspaper sent up a lady reporter, and a male photographer by fast car. The lady reporter, using shorthand, quickly wrote down the story, of how the children had worked together for half an hour to make the snowman. The photographer, asked them all to stand around the giant snowman, while he operated his camera, and took several pictures. The dinner hour was past, and everyone went back into their own school, happier than they had ever been before.

Next morning, in both Worship Assemblies, the children were asked to give the snowman a name. Neither school knew what name the other school would choose. Strangely, both schools chose the same name, "Goliath." Have you any idea why they chose that name?

That week-end, the local newspaper congratulated every member of the two schools, because they had all worked together to build the snowman, instead of fighting each other with snowballs. The two schools had shown the world a good example. The newspaper showed several pictures of happy school children playing in the snow. The newspaper also mentioned that Ben had shown a gift for leadership. Sarah's name was not mentioned, but she was proud of her big brother anyway.

74

The two schools believed that they had a new beginning for two reasons. First, it was a New Year. Secondly, the children had begun to see the pupils from the other school, not as enemies, but as their friends. It really began a new way of thinking for each of them. It was good fun to begin the New Year this way.

Prayer:

> Father, God, we thank you for warm days,
> and we thank you for Winter days.
> We love to play in the snow,
> and to see the white frost on the hedges.
> Teach us to work together in good causes.
> May older children help younger ones.   Amen.

Hymn:

> One more step along the world I go. (C&P. 1. 47) or (J.P. 188)

Teachers' Note: (1) The point of the story is that of the children of both schools making a united effort at the beginning a New Year. (2) Ben showed early signs of leadership. He tried to solve problems and make peace. (3) Older children need to learn to protect the younger ones.

(b) Digging for Gold

Week 1   New Beginnings

Old Bill was a gold prospector, who with many others, was looking for gold-bearing soil, up among the Rocky Mountains of Canada. He lived about 150 years ago, when it was common for people to leave the towns, and to travel the country looking for places to pan for gold. When they found what they believed was gold-bearing rocky soil, they would place the soil in a metal pan, and swill it away, in a nearby stream. The gold being heavier than the soil would lie in the bottom of the washing-pan, after the soil had been washed out of the pan.

It required a lot of skill, to swill the soil out of the pan, but those who had the knack of gold-panning, could become very rich. Usually the gold was found as gold-dust, or gold-nuggets. The prospectors would store up the gold which they found in small leather bags. Later, they brought their little bags to the bank in the town to be weighed. The bank would pay the prospectors good money for the gold.

One day, after long searching in the mountains, old Bill came across a site at the bottom of a small hill. Bill felt sure that this was the gold bearing soil, for which he had been searching. He was all alone, as he began to dig into the clay of the lonely Rockies. There were wild birds of every kind, all around him, especially eagles. Often he could hear the wolves howling at night among the Pine forests. Beavers played in the nearby river.

Nevertheless, Bill dug his trench deep into the hill, because he felt sure that gold was lying, under the ground, and not very far away. Every prospector had a private wish that one day they would strike a large gold seam, and that they would become very rich, instead of having to pan for gold each day.

Sad to say, old Bill dug, looking for gold, for one year. Three hundred and sixty-five days is a long time to dig without any rewards. Bill had begun to give up hope that any gold existed in his trench. He said to himself, "Well, I'll give it another day, and if I cannot find any trace of gold dust, then I'll give it all up, and go home." So he worked very hard that last day, but could not find a trace of gold. All at once, in great anger, Bill threw down his shovel and pick-axe. "I have had enough of all this work, I am going home," he said to himself. "I have wasted more than a year of my life."

Off old Bill went, back to his home-town. He left behind him, the lonely Rocky mountains and all the animals and birds. He did not want to think anymore about the Salmon swimming upstream, after having swam halfway around the oceans of the world. He left behind him the forests of Pine trees. Bill lived a short time after coming home. He died a poor man.

Fifty years passed by, and his grandson, Howard, happened to be going through old papers in the attic at home. He came across an old saddle-bag that once belonged to his grandfather, Bill. Howard opened the saddle-bag, and found an old hand-drawn map inside it. The map showed the river, and the mountains, and the site of a small mine on a hillside. Grandson Howard, decided to go prospecting for gold himself.

Howard travelled, riding on a mule, which also carried his digging tools. After a long journey, he at last found the deserted gold-mine, belonging to his late Grandfather. There, he found the pick-axe, and the shovel, but the wooden handles had rotted away.

Howard, began to dig with his new shovel, just at the place where Old Bill had stopped. On the very first day, Howard had dug through just about one metre of clay, when he came across the biggest gold seam which had ever been seen. Howard, carefully dug out all the gold he could take, and washed it carefully in the stream. It had happened after only one day's digging. Howard realised that he had become a very rich man.

Old Bill never knew, just how near he had been to that gold seam. If he had just spent one more day digging, he would have been a rich man. Maybe, he gave up too easily!

The lesson in this story for children is that, "If at first we don't succeed, we should try, try, and try again!" We may never be digging for gold in the Rocky

Mountains. However, we might be learning a new sport, or a musical instrument, or even a foreign language. The way to succeed is to keep working at our task.

Prayer:

> Heavenly Father, give us all worth-while goals.
> Give us the courage to persist in doing good.
> At the beginning of this New Year,
> help us to resolve to be better people.
> Teach us that God is with us each day,
> each hour, and each minute;
> may we need never be afraid.   Amen.

Hymn:

> What about being old Moses. (C&P. 2. 81)

Teachers' Note: (1) It is good to have an aim in life. Having an aim is something more valuable, than even finding gold. (2) Sometimes a little extra effort on our part, would give us more skills. Practice makes perfect. (3). Children sometimes give up too easily. Did you notice that old Bill's previous digging made it easier for Howard to succeed? Our parents, and teachers try to make life easier for children.

(c) A Blind Man Begins Again   *Week 1   New Beginnings*

Bartimaeus was a blind man, who lived in the city cf Jericho. He sat by the dusty wayside, with a begging bowl in his lap. In those days, there was not much else that a blind man could do. Sometime in the past, Bartimaeus had his sight, and he could see quite normally. Perhaps, as a baby, he had been left out in the harvest field, where his mother worked. It may have been a very hot day, and as the hot sun shone down on the baby, he may have suffered from sun-stroke, and become blind. We do not know: we can only guess, about his blindness. Now in his manhood, he sat and begged in the street, because he could not earn any money to buy his food.

One day, there was a lot of excitement in the street, as people heard that Jesus, the healer, was passing through Jericho. Bartimaeus could hear the approaching crowd of people, as they gathered around Jesus. "What is it?", asked the blind man. "What is happening? Tell me what you can see?" Someone in the crowd, said that Jesus was passing through Jericho.

Bartimaeus realised that his opportunity had come. He shouted with all his voice, "Jesus! Take pity on me." The crowd did not pay any attentionto the blind man and they told him to keep quiet. Bartimaeus, however, began to shout all the louder. "Jesus, have pity on me!"

Jesus called the the blind man over, and said to him, "What do you want me to do for you?" Bartimaeus said, "Lord, I want to see again!" Jesus answered him, "Your faith has made you well." Just at that moment, a miracle happened. Bartimaeus' eyes were healed, and he could see normally, just like everyone else. He was the happiest man in Jericho that day, as he joined the crowd, following Jesus along the street.

Next day, Bartimaeus, did not need to sit begging by the wayside. As a healthy man, he could find a job, and earn his own living. What really had happened was that Jesus gave Bartimaeus a fresh start in life.

Can you imagine the jobs that Bartimaeus might have been able to do? He could have been an artist. He could have been a shepherd, and well able to go searching for lost sheep. If he had become a fisherman, he could have watched the sea gulls hovering over a shoal of fish in the lake. This would have shown him where to drop the fishing nets from a boat. He could have become a watchman on the city wall, just as we have policemen today. One thing is certain. Bartimaeus would want to make good use of his eyes again.

If you ever go to Birmingham Art Gallery, ask to see the artist, Millais' painting, entitled , "The Blind girl." The painting depicts two poor children, sitting together. One is a blind girl who sits and plays her concertina . Her younger sister who has good normal sight, is describing to her blind sister, the colours of a double rainbow across the dark sky. On the shawl of the blind girl, is a beautiful butterfly. You may buy a post-card copy of the painting, and keep it at home, to remind you of the value of your own eyesight.

Prayer:

    Heavenly Father, We are glad that Jesus
    healed blind Bartimaeus.
    We pray for blind children everywhere.
    We thank you for skilled Doctors, and Opticians,
    who make it possible for people to see better.
    We thank you, for the beautiful colours,
    which we see in the flowers, and in the rainbow.   Amen.

Hymn:

    He gave me eyes so I could see. (C&P. 1. 18)

Teachers' Note: (1). Jesus had time both for the crowd, and also for one poor blind beggar. (2). Bartimaeus shouted loudly that day, because be believed Jesus could really work a miracle. (3) Many people suffer from cataracts, which grow over their eyes like a skin, and make them blind. Doctors today, often are able to

78

perform an operation, which can restore sight to such people. That too, is like a miracle for the patient.

(a) The Rescue

Week 2   Water Stories

Today, in this assembly, you are to listen carefully. You may count the number of foolish actions in the story, by holding one of your fingers, when you think that you hear of one foolish deed being mentioned. If you think that you hear of two foolish actions, hold on to two fingers. If there are more, then you must hold more fingers. At the end of the story, if you can remember all the foolish actions, then your assembly Leader may allow you to mention them.

Some teenage boys and girls were walking along the Promenade of a sea-side town. They were enjoying a beautiful day, and looking over the sea wall at the calm sea, The young people sat on one of the long benches, provided by the Town Council. Some of them noticed that on a special kiosk, there was a round, red and white life-belt, hanging up. There was a long rope attached to the life-belt. A painted sign, read, *"For emergency use only."*

Some of the boys took the life-belt off the pole, where it was placed. They used a pen knife to cut through the rope, and then they hung the life-belt back again on the pole. Other members of the young people's group, used the long coil of rope to make a skipping rope. Although they were teenagers, they enjoyed skipping with the rope at the sea wall. Two of them held ends of the long rope, and the others lined up and skipped together, just as children do in a school playing yard. They had good fun.

When they had finished skipping they just threw the rope over the sea wall, where it was washed out to sea. They all went home, thinking that no-one would know about it.

The following week, was a week of very stormy weather. The big waves were crashing over the sea wall at high tide. Sally decided to take her dog, Trixie, for a walk along the Promenade. Trixie ran ahead of Sally, and came to the space in the wall, where there were steps from the promenade, down to sea shore. Just at that moment, a very large wave crashed over the wall, and washed the little dog, Trixie, out to sea. Sally ran to the place where the dog had been washed away, and looking over the wall, there she saw her dog swimming in the water.

Sally was a very good swimmer in the local swimming pool, so without thinking, she foolishly dived off the wall, into the sea. She thought that she could save her beloved Trixie, but the heavy swell and current, carried her along the sea wall. She realised that she could not reach the dog, and that she could not get back again.

A man who was standing looking out to sea, saw what had happened. He ran towards the life-belt hanging up on the post. He found to his dismay that there was no rope attached to the life-belt. He realised that even if Sally gripped the floating life-belt, that he could not pull her to safety. The vandals had taken the rope. Sally continued to swim and float on her back, shouting for help all the time.

By this time a small crowd had gathered. Esther was a Venture Scout, and when she saw the crowd at the sea wall, she ran up to see if she could help. She saw the man holding the lifebelt, and wondering what to do. She shouted to the man, "don't throw the lifebelt just yet, or you will lose it". Esther ran across the road to the back of a hotel, and there were some table cloths hanging on a clothes line. Esther pulled the table cloths off the line, and in a few seconds she had taken the clothes line off the poles. She quickly rolled the strong line into a loose coil, and without looking right or left, she ran back across the road, to the sea wall.

Esther was out of breath, but she quickly tied a bowline knot on the line around the life-belt. Pushing everyone to the one side, Esther ran along the sea wall to the point where the sea current had carried Sally. With a shout, Esther threw the life-belt out to Sally in the rushing tide. Sally swam towards the life-belt, and put it over her head. Then she put her arms around it, and began to kick with her legs.

Esther, the Venture Scout, tightened the line, and began to pull Sally and the life-belt along to an opening in the sea wall, where there were more steps. Soon, Sally had clambered up the steps, and Esther wrapped her coat around her to prevent heat loss. Someone in the crowd had enough presence of mind to "phone 999 for the ambulance. Soon, the ambulance arrived, and Sally was rushed off to hospital. Everyone in the crowd cheered Esther, and she returned the compliment by giving the Scout salute!

Esther, ran along the promenade to find out what had happened to Trixie, Sally's little dog. She could not see a dog in the water anywhere. Esther knew that dogs were very good swimmers, so she ran past the harbour to the South Shore, and there was Trixie, walking along the sand. The dog had rescued herself on the low beach. Esther cuddled the little dog, and took her home. She left the clothes line on the sand, and never told the Hotel-owner why she had thrown the table-cloths off the clothes line. Sally, that evening was allowed home from hospital. She visited Esther to thank her for her rescue, and to collect her beloved dog, Trixie.

There were Four Foolish Actions. Children who are holding on to four fingers are correct.

(a)   The Teenagers should not have taken the life-belt rope.

(b)   Sally should not have dived into the rough sea to attempt to rescue Trixie.

(c)   Esther did not look right or left, when she ran back across the road. She might have been knocked down by a car.

(d)   Esther, did not go back to the Hotel-owner to explain, why she had taken the clothes line.

Prayer:

Lord, may we never be cruel to animals,
but always treat them as God's creatures.
Save us from ever becoming vandals.
Give us all the commonsense,
never to take any foolish risks that might harm us.
May we become reliable helpers
to others in trouble or in need.   Amen.

Hymn:

In the morning early, I go down to the sea. (C&P. 1. 60)

Teachers' Note: The point of the story is that we are to think before we act. (1) When the Teenagers took the rope, they became thoughtless vandals. (2) Hasty actions are dangerous. Sally did not think before she acted. (3) Esther, the Venture Scout, acted quickly, calmly, and correctly in the actual emergency.

(b) The Three Wells   *Week 2   Water Stories*

We begin with a joke today! Betty said to Tom, "Have you heard the story of the three wells?" Tom answered, "No, I haven't heard the story of the three wells. Please, tell it to me!" Betty said, (very slowly) "Well! Well! Well!"

Seriously now! We are briefly going to hear three stories about real wells.

The Secret Well

George and his young school friends were being shown through the old Norman castle at Carrickfergus, in County Antrim, in the North of Ireland. The castle is built on rocks, partly in the sea, and close beside the harbour. The castle Attendant showed the party round the walls, and then he said, to George and his friends, "We are going into the fortified tower. I will show you the secret of the strength, of Carrickfergus castle."

George and his friends, followed the Attendant. They had no idea what they were about to see. They climbed up the spiral stone steps into the square tower. They nearly fell on the "trip step". (A step deliberately built higher than the other steps, in a dark part of the staircase, intended to trip up enemies, who would not know about it, if they managed to get inside the castle.)

Now they were in a large room overlooking the courtyard below. The Attendant, pointed out an iron ring in the floor. He pulled up a trap door, and said, "Here is the secret of the strength of this castle." There below them was a deep well, hidden in the middle of the castle. The castle had been built over a fresh water-spring in the rock, close beside the salt water of the sea. When an enemy army surrounded the castle for a long time, the Norman soldiers had only to let down a bucket, inside their tower, in order to obtain pure drinking water.

George and his school friends understood what the Attendant had been telling them. No-one can live without water, therefore, it is always good to be prepared for what we need most in life.

The Dark Well

The Second story is about a country boy, who was walking past a neighbour's farm one dark evening, when he fell down a well. As he fell, he managed to hold on to the sides of the well. He looked down, and could see nothing but darkness. He thought to himself, "This looks to be a deep well. I'll better hold on, in case I drown." He shouted for help, but no one heard his cries.

He worried for more than an hour, and then his arms became so tired, holding on to the stones at the side of the well, that at last, he had to let go. To his surprise, he fell only a few centimetres, because the well was not deep after all. To his relief, he found that the well was dry. The moon began to shine, brightening the darkness. The boy soon climbed out of the well, and went safely home. The point in this story is that, often we worry about things which might never happen. This well was dry, anyway! There is an old saying, "All is well that ends well!"

Ann's Well

The third story is Canadian. There was once an Irish girl who lived in Canada. She was known as, "Holy Ann," because she believed in praying about ordinary matters. She worked for a harsh farmer. There was no water at the farm, because the well beside the house had dried up. The farmer made Ann carry water back to the house, from a well, nearly one mile away. She had to fetch the water each day up a steep hill, and the climb made her very tired. Ann read in her Bible, (Isaiah 41;18), "I will make rivers flow on dry hills, and springs in the valleys." So she prayed that God would understand how tired she was, and that he would create a spring on their dry farm.

Next morning, instead of going down the hill to the far-away well, she went to the old dried up well beside the house. When she looked down into it, she discovered that it was no longer dry. Quite naturally, a spring had begun to produce a bubbling flow of pure water in the well beside the house. (Maybe, the well had resumed its flow after the rains, and no-one had noticed it before.)

However, Ann took the return of the bubbling spring in the well to be an answer to her prayers. She would no longer have to walk two miles to fetch water.

Sometimes we can answer our own prayers by having a closer look at our problem.

Nowadays, we admire the International Charities, which send water engineers to provide new wells and pumps for villages in dry Third World countries. These water engineers answer the prayers of people overseas, by providing pure water for them. Who is to say that God is not behind it all!

Prayer:

> Heavenly Father, we are grateful for the pure water
> which we enjoy in our homes.
> We pray that you will bless the International Charities,
> as they provide new wells and pumps,
> for people in Third World countries.
> May we learn not to waste water.   Amen.

Hymn:

> Have you heard the raindrops drumming on the roof-tops. (C&P. 1. 2)

Teachers' Notes: (1) The secret well inside Carrickfergus castle came from someone's good fore-sight before the castle was built. No-one inside the castle would ever need to die of thirst. (2) In the dark well story, who was to blame? The farmer who left the well without a lid, or the boy's own lack of watchfulness? (3) Ann looked next morning at the well she had not used for a long time. Sometimes, God answers our prayers, by helping us to take a closer look at a problem.

(c) A Baby in a Basket   *Week 2   Water Stories*

The Hebrew people had become slaves in the land of Egypt. The hard-hearted Egyptian slave-masters beat the Hebrew slaves daily with whips. The Hebrews were forced to make bricks from clay, under the hot sun. Straw was needed to mix with the clay, in order that the clay bricks held together, as they lay on the the ground. It was the heat of the sun that baked the bricks hard.

The reason for the Hebrew people becoming slaves was that four hundred years before, Joseph the Hebrew, became the great ruler of Egypt. He was next to Pharaoh in power. His family were highly honoured in those days. After Joseph and his family died, the Hebrew people increased. Families increased, so that after four hundred years had passed, there were thousands of Hebrew people in Egypt. The Egyptians noticed that the people were increasing, and they became afraid that the Hebrews might become so many, that they could take over, and become rulers of Egypt.

This fear was the reason that the Egyptians made the Hebrew people work as slaves. The Egyptians became very cruel to the Hebrews. The slaves cried out in their prayers to the Lord, because he was their God. (Hebrews later in history were called "Jews").

Some Egyptians suggested to Pharoah, that all baby boys who were born into Hebrew homes, should be killed. This they thought would prevent the slaves becoming a large army in years to come. Therefore, for many years, all the little baby boys were killed, but little girls were spared.

There was one Hebrew family, into which a baby boy was born. The family did not want their baby to be killed. The baby's mother asked her husband to make her a little basket, and to paint it inside with thick tar. The tar was applied thickly, and when it dried, it became so hard, that it kept out water. The basket being water-tight, floated just like a small boat.

The family went down to the river Nile, which is a very wide river, with high bulrushes growing along its edges. They carefully placed the baby inside the basket, and hid the basket, floating, among the reeds and bulrushes. Miriam, the baby's elder sister, sat on the bank of the river Nile, a short distance away. In this way, she was able to guard the baby, in case he might cry our loudly, and his crying might attract attention. The baby's life was always in danger.

The royal Princess, who was the daughter of Pharoah, the King, was walking along the river one day, with her ladies. They heard the baby crying, and soon they found the little baby boy, in his basket, hidden and floating among the reeds. The Princess said, "It must be one of the babies belonging to the Hebrew slaves. It is a beautiful little boy. I will take it home to my palace. I think that I will call this baby, "Moses" because that means "drawn out." (of the water)!"

Miriam, the baby's elder sister, saw what had happened, so she made up a clever plan immediately. Miriam ran up to the Princess, and asked whether the baby they had found, would need a nurse? She offered her services. In this wonderful way, Miriam, became the nurse to the little baby, and she was paid wages by the King actually for nursing her own brother. The baby would always be safe.

No one at that time knew why God had allowed the baby Moses to be brought up in Pharoah's palace. The child was taught everything that a Prince should know. However, God had a plan for this special baby. He grew up, and became Moses the Prince of Egypt. Later, he rebelled against the cruel treatment given to the Hebrew slaves, who were really his own people.

He became the National leader of the Hebrews. One night, Moses led thousands of the Hebrew people out of Egypt. Every man, woman and child, escaped, walking through the through the Red sea on dry land, after a great East wind had blown back the tide. They began their long journey to the Promised Land. It was described as a "land flowing with milk and honey," which means that it was a fruitful country in which to live. It all began, because a baby boy was saved from the river Nile. Just think of it! Every great leader, was once a helpless baby!

Prayer:

> Lord God, we are happy that the baby Moses
> was saved from the river Nile.
> Bless and protect all baby boys and girls.
> May we set them a good example,
> by our own good conduct, and thoughtfulness.
> We are joyful, because this story,
> also reminds us of the birth of Jesus Christ.   Amen.

Hymn:

> Travel on, travel on. (C&P. 1. 42)

Teachers' Note: (1) God prepared to help the Hebrew slaves by protecting a baby, who was to be their future leader. (2). Miriam was allowed to nurse the baby in Pharaoh's palace, for a long time, and she was paid by the Egyptians for doing it. (3) Moses would never forget what happened at the Nile, since his name, means "drawn out" (of the water). God loves all babies everywhere.

(a) Banquets and Birthdays   *Week 3   Invitations*

Jesus told this story. There was once a rich man who had arranged a banquet. His servants prepared the large feast. Then he sent out invitations to his guests, expecting them to accept his kind invitation to attend. At the time of the feast, he sent another servant to tell his guests, "Come for everything is now ready"

However, the people whom had been invited, did not want to attend the feast. They all began to make their excuses. The first guest, replied, "I have just bought a field, and I must go and inspect it. Please, excuse me!" Another guest replied, "I have just bought five yoke of oxen. I must go and try them out. Please, excuse me." Yet another, replied, "I have just been married. Please, excuse me."

The servant arrived back, and reported their answers to his master. The rich man was very angry. He said to his servant, "Go out quickly into the streets and alleys of the town, and bring into my banquet, the poor people, the lame people, and the blind. Let them enjoy my feast." The servant came back to his master. He reported that he had done as he had been ordered, but there was yet room for more people.

His master sent his servant out again, saying, "Go out into the main roads, and into the smaller lanes, and make people come in, so that my house may be full. I tell you, that not one of those people, whom I invited, shall have any part in my banquet."

Jesus explained the meaning of the story. (See Luke 14. v. 12, 13.) He said, that some people invite others to a celebration, or a meal, in order that they may get an invitation back. When you want to do good, then invite those poor, or handicapped people who cannot repay you, and God will bless you.

Now, everyone may consider the second story, which is about our own times, and see if there are points, which remind us of the Bible parable.

Gemma was ten years of age on her next birthday, which was the 11th. June. The evenings after tea-time were lovely and warm, with long hours of daylight. She talked to her Mum about her birthday party. She had decided to invite six girls and six boys from her class at school, to attend the party on the following Friday evening. Gemma's parents had spent a lot of money in order to provide a lovely meal, and also they had booked places at the Bowling Alley across the road.

The day before the party, four of the boys who had been invited, read in the newspaper that there was an exciting new film being shown in the local Cinema on the evening of the Birthday Party. The four boys decided to go to the Cinema , instead. Worse still, they did not tell Gemma, nor her parents. They decided to go to the cinema, despite having replied to Gemma's beautiful invitation cards, saying that they would attend the party. On the Friday evening, all six girls turned up, but only two boys.

Gemma and her parents were rather disappointed. Gemma's Dad spoke up. He said, "The Institute for the Blind are holding an evening class on Friday evenings. I think that they teach the blind children touch type-writing." Blind young people can type their school work, faster than sighted children can write. Blind people use the word "Sighted" to describe others, who see normally.

Dad went on talking. "Let us invite the group of young people from the Institute to our party. Then we can take them across the road to the Bowling Alley for the rest of the evening." Everyone thought that this was a splendid idea! Dad telephoned up the Instructor at the Institute, which was quite near. "Yes," the Instructor answered across the telephone, "there are five young people here just now. It is such a lovely Summer evening, I am sure that they would be delighted to attend your Party, rather than sitting here learning to type letters. Can you guarantee that they all will get home safely?" Dad assured the Instructor, that the Institute group would be home before 10 p.m.

In less than half an hour, Gemma's party had increased to fourteen happy young people. There were six girls, and two boys from school, with five others from the Institute, which adds up to thirteen. Of course, Gemma herself was the fourteenth member. After a bumper party, and a few games, the party moved across the road to the Bowling Alley.

They all had a happy evening together. The Blind children were excited, when they knocked the skittles down with their bowls. They laughed and enjoyed themselves all evening. The time arrived for all the party to go home by car. Gemma was sure that this party was the best that she had ever enjoyed. Trevor, a blind boy, said, "Gemma, why don't you invite us back next year!" Gemma had learned that blind young people can have just as much fun as sighted children.

Prayer:

Loving Father, we thank you for the parables of Jesus.
We are glad that Jesus loved handicapped people.
May we make other people welcome in our lives,
to share our happiness.
Teach us good manners,
and consideration for others.
Bless everyone who is less fortunate than we are.   Amen.

Hymn:

Would you walk by on the other side. (C&P. 1. 70)

Teachers' Note: (1) "Welcome" is a lovely warm-hearted word. (2) Jesus taught us to be considerate to other people, and not to look for rewards for doing good. (3) Gemma's party was accidently like the Bible story. Yet we must always remember that blind people are as normal as sighted people. They do not like anyone to pity them. Reference: Luke Chap. 14. verses 12-24.

(b) The Writing on the Wall   *Week 3   Invitations*

When Belshazzar became the new King of Babylon, he held a great banquet. He invited a thousand of his princes and nobles, with their wives, to join him. He drank wine with them. King Belshazzar ordered that the Temple gold and silver cups should be used. These cups had been stolen by his father's army from God's Temple in Jerusalem, when the city had been captured.

Jewish people in those days, thought that Belshazzer had acted very wrongly in using the Temple cups. To them, it appeared even worse, when his friends having filled the cups with wine, they praised the idols which had been made by men's hands from gold, silver, bronze, iron, and wood. To the Jews, it was as if the Babylonians were trying to insult the living God of the Jewish Temple.

Then something frightening happened at the banquet. Suddenly, a hand appeared, and began to write on the plaster of the wall, above the table. The hand wrote the words, "MENE MENE TEKEL PARSIN." The king was so frightened that his face turned grey with fear, and his knees began to knock together, and his legs gave way under him.

Belshazzar called the wisest men in Babylon, and offered them a reward for being able to read the writing on the wall, and to explain its meaning. He offered any of the wise men the honour of being dressed in purple, and of wearing a gold chain around his neck, and becoming the third highest ruler in the land. However, none of the wise Babylonians could read the message on the wall. At this the king began to be even more frightened.

The Queen came in at that moment, and said, "Do not be afraid. There is one man in this kingdom who could read the meaning of this message. When your father, Nebuchadnezzar was alive, he appointed a Jew by the name of Daniel, to be a chief ruler. He can understand dreams and such problems. I advise you to call for Daniel, and he will explain to you the meaning of the writing on the wall."

When Daniel arrived before King Belshazzar, he was promised rewards. Daniel answered that he did not want rewards for reading the mysterious message. Daniel explained, "O King, God has been good to your father, King Nebuchadnezzar, and made him a great Emperor over many people.

Yet your father became very proud, as if it he had become great by his own power. God was angry with him. Your father slowly became mad. He began to act like an animal. He even lived with the wild donkeys, and ate grass like the cattle.

Now he is dead, and gone, you are doing worse things.

You have set yourself against the God of Heaven. God is angry with you, because you have disgracefully mis-used the gold and silver cups from his Temple. You do not honour the true God. It was God who made that hand to write on the wall."

Daniel said, "MENE" means that God will bring your kingdom to an end. "TEKEL" means that you have been weighed on the scales and you have been found short-weight. "PARSIN" means that God will divide your kingdom, and give it to the Medes and Persians." King Belshazzer, rewarded Daniel for being able to read the writing on the wall, and made him third ruler in the land.

That very night, the army of his enemy, King Darius, stopped up a stream of water going under the city wall. This left a dry path under the walls. King Darius secretly led his Persian army under the walls into the city. He captured Babylon, and Belshazzar was killed by the Persian soldiers, just as the writing on the wall had foretold.

Prayer:

Lord God, help us to respect churches,
chapels, mosques, synagogues, and temples.
We rejoice because you are the Father of us all.
When we assemble together in school,
may we value our school building.
Make our hearts your holy house.
Bless every girl and boy here today.   Amen.

Hymn:

The ink is black, the page is white. (C&P. 1. 67)

Teachers' Note: (1) Belshazzar became a proud king, and did not serve his people well. (2) He had no respect for the holy cups which his father had stolen from the Jewish Temple at Jerusalem. (3) The hand writing on the wall became a warning from God, that Belshazzar's evil reign would come to a end in disaster.

A Teachers' further note on exegesis

The Teacher will face the difficulty of interpreting for him/herself, before telling the story about the appearance of the hand writing on the wall. It would not be difficult to explain the story from a psychological perspective, since we see with our minds. (Visions are part of Old Testament explanations of how God speaks to people. The New Testament also includes visions and dreams, but adds that true revelation comes through the Holy Spirit). At this *literal level,* the story is a simple introduction for children, to Hebrew Holy Scriptures. From the *Historian's perspective,* it is an illustration of how Old Testament writers treated psychological phenomena. From a *Judaistic perspective,* Daniel had a prophet's gifts, being a "Seer," offering a spiritual prognosis for his own age. History confirms that he was correct in foretelling the fall of Babylon.) Reference: Daniel 5.

(c) Water into Wine   *Week 3   Invitations*

There was a wedding in the village of Cana, which is situated in Galilee. Jesus and his mother, Mary, had been invited. The disciples were also to be guests, so it was a very happy occasion. The Bride and Bridegroom, and their friends were enjoying a very pleasant time together, when there was a disaster in the kitchen. (People in that part of the world did not drink tea or coffee at their meals. Instead, they drank wine mixed with water, or water alone.) Mary, the mother of Jesus came up to him very quietly. She whispered in his ear, "They have run short of wine".

Jesus turned to his mother, whom he loved dearly, and said, "Dear woman, do not involve me in this problem. My time has not yet arrived." (This sounds rather abrupt in English, but the tone of voice used can make it more tenderly spoken). Nevertheless, Mary, who had a great faith in her son, whispered to the servants, "You just do whatever he tells you."

There were six stone water jars which had been placed quite near them. The jars held more than one hundred litres each, (between 20 and 30 gallons), so they were were rather large. The Jews used these large jars for water to wash their hands and feet. Jesus said to the servants, "Fill up the jars with water". The servants filled the jars with water, right up to the brim. By a miracle, the water was changed into wine.

Jesus said, "Take a cup of this wine to the Master of Ceremonies at the wedding." The Master of Ceremonies, tasted the new wine. He did not know where the wine had come from, although the servants were aware of what had happened.

He called the Bridegroom to the one side. He remarked, "Everyone usually brings out the best wine first, then the cheaper wine is served after everyone has drank quite a lot. Yet, you, have saved the best wine to the very end."

This miracle in Cana, was the very first miracle, which Jesus had ever performed. In performing this sign, Jesus showed the glory of God within himself. As a result, the faith of his twelve disciples increased.

An explanation which may have optional value in some classes.

When we consider wine, we must remember that there are two kinds of wine. There is **alcoholic** wine, and there is **non-alcoholic wine.**

There are at least three attitudes to alcoholic drink among adults.

First, there are Total Abstainers. These are people who do not use alcoholic wine in any form, (except, perhaps, on rare occasions as a medicine).

Secondly, there are Moderate Drinkers. These are people who drink with self discipline. They also may drink wine at meals.

Thirdly, there are Alcoholics. These are people who have become dependent on alcoholic drink. They need medical help.

Religious people all have some conscience about using alcoholic drink because it may make us lose our self-control. We know that the Law advises against drivers drinking and driving. When workers operate machinery, or drive trains or buses in their employment, they are forbidden to drink alcoholic liquor. Sports-people often make a decision, not to use alcoholic drink, because it harms their best performance on the sports field. We all must decide our own attitude to wine, when we understand the problem.

Prayer:

We are happy Lord,
because Jesus and his Mother, Mary,
attended a village wedding.
We pray that you will always be the centre
of our most happy events.
Bless , O Father, all weddings, and family life.
Satisfy the needs of hungry
and unhappy people.   Amen.

Hymn:

Thank you Lord for this new day. (C&P. 1) or (J.P. 232)

Teachers' Note: The Jews, in those days, often drank wine mixed with several parts of water. (1) Jesus attended a happy wedding, with his mother and friends. (2) He supplied the shortage of wine, which must have been an embarrassment to the bridal party. (3) Children may be able to recognise the various attitudes to using wine, and to the dangers of unrestrained alcoholic drinking. Later they will have to make their own personal religious decisions about it. (Ref: John Ch. 2. 1-11).

An additional Teachers' note.

This is a difficult story to understand, for two reasons. First , because it is the report of a miracle (sign), and secondly, because, the author, of St. John, often writes with a secondary spiritual meaning. Why did Jesus provide such a large amount of wine for the wedding? There were six stone pots, full to the brim. Maybe, the wine was shared out with other non-attenders afterwards. Many scholars believe the story to be symbolic. The water signifies the Jewish religion, and that the new wine signifies the new religion which Jesus brings.

In the real world, attitudes to drink do not fall neatly into three categories. Our attitudes are formed by home-backgrounds, country of origin, culture, or religious belief. etc.

(a) Terry Waite's Postcard   *Week 4   Sending Messages*

Tinkers were travelling metal workers, who could make or repair pots and pans on their horse drawn waggons. Many of them lived in towns. John Bunyan was the son of one of these tinkers. He was born in the Bedfordshire village of Elstow. He lived during the seventeenth century (1628-88). Even as a boy, he read many books, and most of all he read the Bible.

John Bunyan enlisted in Oliver Cromwell's army, when Parliament and King Charles I fought against each other, in the English Civil War. Oliver Cromwell was a Puritan Christian. He became Leader of the Parliamentary army. When serving under him as a soldier, John Bunyan became a Christian. Bunyan was influenced by the talk of other Christian soldiers. He was discharged from the army in 1647. He married and set up a Christian home.

John Bunyan became a Baptist nonconformist Preacher, and because he was not an Anglican Priest, he felt free to preach anywhere and everywhere. He took his religion very seriously. He experienced many visions, as he repented from his sins. People came in crowds to hear Bunyan preaching.

When King Charles II became the new king, a law was passed, (The Conventicle Act 1664), forbidding more than five people to worship God together, unless they used the Church of England Prayer Book. John Bunyan being a Baptist Preacher, would not obey this unkind law. He just carried on preaching. The authorities put Bunyan in Bedford prison for twelve years.

He was often offered freedom, if he would stop preaching. He refused. Even in prison he preached to the other prisoners. Bunyan also wrote books in prison. Several of his famous books were published. One was called "Grace Abounding", and another was entitled "The Pilgrim's Progress." Although a prisoner, John Bunyan made laces, and sold them at the prison door. In this way, he was able to provide money to buy food for his family at home.

When the Law allowed Bunyan out of prison after twelve years, he continued his preaching and writing. Many people, were helped by his preaching, and they believed in Jesus. Years passed by. In 1688, Bunyan was travelling by horseback, through the pouring rain. He was trying to reach a father who had been quarrelling with his son. He wanted to persuade them to make peace and to be friends again.

Sadly, John Bunyan on his long horse-ride through the rain became soaked to the skin. At the end of the journey, he became very ill, and quickly died. The important point to remember about John Bunyan is that he loved his Lord, and that he had been ready to go to prison for twelve years, rather than obey a bad law.

In our life-time, Terry Waite, became the Archbishop of Canterbury's special representative. While Terry was in Lebanon, he was captured, and he became a political prisoner in Beruit. Terry was locked up, entirely alone, in a cell, for four long years. He never saw anyone, nor spoke to anyone, except, perhaps, a short word, when a guard brought food to him.

Then one day, a guard unexpectedly brought a postcard to him. The postcard had been sent by some unknown Christian person, whom Terry had never met. It showed a picture of a stained glass window from Bedford, depicting John Bunyan in prison.

Terry turned the card over, and read the message from the unknown person. It read, "We remember. We shall not forget. We shall continue to pray for you, and to work for all people who are detained around the world." Terry, being a good Anglican, understood the significance of the card showing John Bunyan. Terry felt that he too was like Bunyan, and that he would be released from jail in time.

Was it not a kind-hearted, thoughtful, action by someone, somewhere, to take the trouble, to send that postcard to Terry? It brought great comfort to him. He longed for the same freedom, that John Bunyan had lost. When Terry was set free from his prison, he felt that he had to tell people about receiving the John Bunyan postcard.

Prayer:

> Lord, we thank you for brave Christian people,
> such as John Bunyan and Terry Waite.
> Bless all the kind people who write to prisoners.
> We earnestly pray for prisoners of conscience,
> of all religions.
> Teach us to be grateful for our own freedom.　Amen.

Hymn:

> Peace perfect peace, is the gift of Christ our Lord. (C&P. 1. 53).

Teachers' Note: (1) John Bunyan took his religion very seriously. We wonder how his good wife and family coped, during his long imprisonment. (2) John Bunyan was a Baptist, but by his example, he later provided a comfort to Terry Waite, a respected Anglican church member. We may all learn from each other. (3) People, even children, from many churches, became a worldwide chain of prayer, praying for Terry Waite's release, just as people long ago prayed for John Bunyan.

(b) Message in a Bottle　　　　*Week 4　Sending Messages*

A 'see-through' plastic bottle containing a message may be displayed as a focus for the Assembly. The actual message may be read out at an appropriate time.

Olga and Olaf were brother and sister. They were Norwegian children, and both of them were studying English at their village school. Many schools in Norway teach the English language from an early age. Their lovely village was on the North Sea coast, and behind the village were high snow-capped mountains.

During the Winter, snow covered much of the country, but during the Spring and Summer, the weather was much like that of Scotland, or Northern England.

Unknown to the Norwegian children, across the North Sea on the Scottish coast, there were two children, by the name of Ian, and Fiona. They too went to school, but they had not begun to study a language. They lived in a cottage beside the sea, quite near, North Berwick. Both of the children were bird-watchers. They wrote down in a notebook the names of the different birds they saw on the seashore. Once, they saw a racing pigeon with a message attached to its leg. That set them thinking.

As they walked along the shore, Ian said to Fiona, "I have an idea. Let us get a clear plastic lemonade bottle, and put a message inside it. We could carefully seal the top of the bottle, to keep out the water. Then we could throw it into the sea, and it might be carried by the wind and sea currents to some faraway country. We could put our names and address on a letter, and who knows, someone might find the bottle, and open it, and read our message." Fiona, replied, "I think that is a jolly good idea. It is like having a real adventure. We will keep everything a secret, and no one will know about it."

So the two Scottish children went straight home. Fiona brought out her school exercise book but she could not think of anything sensible to write. Her brother had no ideas either. Ian looked up at a Church calender on the wall, beside the door. The calender had a passage from the Bible printed on it. Ian said, "Let us copy that passage from the calender, and put our name and address on it." "A good idea" said Fiona, "Since we do not know who might find the plastic bottle. A Bible passage might be helpful to someone." Ian wrote out the words.

They added their names and address, and put the paper inside the clear plastic bottle. Then they sealed the bottle, to keep its message dry. Next morning they went down to the rocks at North Berwick. Fiona threw the bottle as far as she could into the choppy sea. Fortunately, the wind was blowing off-shore. The wind, and sea seemed to carry the plastic bottle off immediately. They did not use a glass bottle, because it might be broken on the rocks and later cut bathers in the sea.

Six months passed by. The two Scottish children did not hear anything more about their plastic bottle. Away over in Norway, Olga and Olaf were feeling rather down-hearted because their beloved Auntie Grethel, had become very ill, and, had died rather suddenly. Olga and Olaf's parents were also feeling rather sad. After a big storm at sea, Olaf said to Olga, "Let us go down to the shore with our trolley. There will be plenty of fire-wood to collect and store for the Winter."

As the two Norwegian children were gathering fire-wood on their trolly, they saw a clear plastic bottle floating in the sea, with a letter inside it. The Norwegian children were ever so excited, as they brought the bottle home to their parents. They opened the bottle, and the two children read the words in English.

(TEACHER AT THIS POINT, MAY OPEN THE BOTTLE, AND READ THE MESSAGE ALOUD.)

Jesus said, *"Look at the birds of the air: they neither sow nor reap, nor store away in barns, and yet your heavenly Father feeds them. Are you not much more valuable than they? Which one of you by worrying, can add a single hour to his life?" Matthew Chapter 6 verses 26.* Olga and Olaf said almost at the same moment, "That is a verse from the English Bible."

The two children translated the verse from English into Norwegian. The parents of the two children were pleased to receive the message. Father said, "It is as if God himself had sent us a message from the Bible that will give us comfort, at the death of our beloved Auntie Grethel. These words mean that we are to stop worrying, because God will take care of Auntie Grethel, even though she has been taken from us. Just think, the message came across the sea in a bottle! Let us write a letter to the two young people whose names are on the paper." So, they did!

Ian and Fiona early one morning received a letter with a Norwegian postage stamp on it. They read a letter of thanks. The passage from St. Matthew's Gospel had brought the Norwegian family a message of comfort at the death of their loved one. The letter also contained an invitation for the whole family to come over on holiday to Norway to meet Olga and Olaf, and their parents. It was exciting!

Soon, both families met, first of all in Norway, and later they met on a return visit in Scotland. Olga and Olaf could speak good English, but Ian and Fiona could not say a word in Norwegian. The Scottish children made up their minds, that when they went up to the Secondary School, that they would try and learn at least one other language. They had not realised just how much the Bible passage would bring comfort at a time of bereavement. "Maybe we were guided by God," said Fiona, "and we did not realise it."

Prayer:

Father God, we thank you for the Scriptures.
When we are sad, let your word
bring us strength and comfort.
Help us, as children to read, and understand
the stories about Jesus Christ.
We are very grateful for God's missionaries,
who long ago, brought the Bible to our country.   Amen.

Hymn:

In the morning early I go down to the sea. (C&P. 1. 60)

Teachers' Note: (1) Ian and Fiona must have lived in a Christian home, because they had a calender bearing a scripture passage printed on it. (2) The message in the bottle, was another method of spreading good news around the world. (A form of media). (3) Sometimes a poem, hymn, or a Bible verse, will bring us fresh hope, when we think about the words.

(c) **Martha's Message**   *Week 4   Sending Messages*

About two miles outside Jerusalem, there was the village of Bethany. Jesus used to call there to visit Mary and Martha, and their brother Lazarus. Jesus sometimes stayed overnight with the family, because he had no home of his own. He became very good friends of the family. Martha, the elder of the two sisters used to be delighted to prepare a meal for Jesus. She had a quick brain, but she was rather fussy, because she wanted to provide the best meal she could for their visitor.

On the other hand, Mary was good at conversation, and she used to sit and talk with Jesus, just to make him feel at home. Martha used to get a little angry, and one day she said to Jesus, "Tell Mary to get up and help me to prepare the meal." Jesus answered, "Martha you are busy about so many things. This time, Mary has chosen to do the better thing. She is good listener."

After Jesus had left again, the family would go back to its usual way of life. It happened that Lazarus suddenly fell ill. Martha, the busy member of the family sent a message to Jesus to come quickly. They knew that he was a healer. However, instead of coming quickly to the family he loved, Jesus remained where he was for another two days. The strange fact was that Jesus knew in himself that Lazarus had died. He said to his disciples, "Lazarus has fallen asleep." Then he said, "I am the resurrection and the life; he who believes in me, even though he were dead, he shall live."

By the time Jesus arrived at Marthas and Mary's home in Bethany, Lazarus had been dead for four days. Martha said, "Lord, if you had been here, Lazarus would not have died." Mary and Martha, along with the other family friends were crying, because Lazarus had died. Jesus also began to cry because he loved Lazarus as a very good friend.

They reached the tomb, which had a stone in front of it. Jesus said, "Roll the stone back." Martha did not like what was happening, because the body had been lying in the grave for four days. She said, "The body will smell." Jesus said to

Martha, "Did I not tell you, that if you believed, that you would see the glory of God".

Then Jesus called, "Lazarus, come out." A figure appeared, bandaged in grave clothes, from head to foot. He could hardly walk. It was Lazarus! Jesus said to the friends, "Take off the grave bandages, and set him free." The friends unwrapped the grave cloths from Lazarus.

Mary and Martha were ever so happy that Lazarus had been restored to life again. The friends who had seen what had happened, believed that Jesus had been sent from God. However, when the religious leaders, known as "Pharisees" and "Chief Priests" in Jerusalem heard about it, they said, "We must put a stop to this." From that day onwards, they made plans to kill Jesus.

Prayer:

> Again, Our Father, we thank you,
> for the Bible stories about the love of Jesus.
> May there be many more homes,
> like the home of Mary and Martha,
> where Jesus Christ is honoured.
> It makes us glad that Jesus loved family life.
> May our school become like one large family.   Amen.

Hymn:

> God is love; His the care. (C&P. 1. 36).

Teachers' Note: (1) Family life is the place to love and respect each other, and also to honour God. (2) Everyone loves Mary, because she was a good listener. Yet, it was Martha's message to Jesus that helped the situation. Martha seems to have been an active thinker. Both kinds of people are good to have in any home. (4). The raising of Lazarus from the dead, reminds us of the Easter story.

A Teachers' further note. The miracle of the raising of Lazarus from the dead, is the author of St. John's presentation of another of the "signs" revealing the power of Jesus. Miracles in Matthew, Mark, and Luke are described by the use of the word (dunamis) meaning a "work of power". The author of John's Gospel uses a different word, (Semeion), meaning "a sign". When St. John's Gospel presents a miracle, the author is using it in a developed manner, as a sign of the purposes of God. Ref. John Chapter 11.)

(a) Two Silly Geese   *Week 5   Anger*

Farmer Berg and Farmer Evans were the best friends in the world. They both had large farms on the prairie land of Canada. The prairies are vast areas of flat countryside. Often these farms have large wheat fields many miles square, and without hedges. The Berg and the Evans families each owned a splendid wooden farm house, not far from each other. The individual members of the families were also good friends. Then something happened, which for a time, spoilt their friendship.

The two farmers took their children each morning, by car to the school house, which was built near the prairie lane. The school was about three miles distant. The two cars arrived at the school house usually about the same time. When the Berg children and the Evans children went into school, their fathers usually reversed their cars in front of the school. Then, they would return home again.

One morning, after the children had gone into school, both farmers reversed their cars, going in a backward circle at the same moment. Neither of the farmers were looking into their driving mirrors. Suddenly, there was a loud crashing sound, and both cars had bumped into each other. Both farmers jumped out, and looked at the back of their cars. Sad to say, both rear ends of the cars were bashed inwards, and the rear lights were also smashed to pieces.

Both farmers were very angry. Farmer Berg blamed Farmer Evans for careless driving. Farmer Evans blamed Farmer Berg for not paying due attention to what was behind him. They forgot that they were friends, and both began to argue fiercely. "Farmer Berg said, "Look at the mess you have made. I will go tomorrow morning, and see my Lawyer. He will take you to court, and you will have to pay money to repair the damage you have done".

Farmer Evans also became angry. He said, "Of all the cheek! You were the one who caused this accident. I will be the one, who is going to see the Lawyer tomorrow. He will present my side of the argument, and the Judge will make you pay for your very poor driving." Both farmers just glared at each other, and went home, without speaking another word. They were boiling with anger.

When Sunday came round, usually the two families sat together in a long pew in the Chapel. However, this Sunday, the Berg family sat in a pew, on the other side of the Chapel, while the Evans family sat on the back pew. The Farmers would not speak or look at each other. The Farmers' wives, and their children, did not feel any anger. They smiled at each other across the Chapel, in their usual friendly way.

Next morning, Farmer Berg drove ten miles into town, and told his Lawyer what had happened. His Lawyer said that he would bring the matter before the Police and the Court. He warned Farmer Berg that he would have to pay fees to him as his Lawyer, and that if he lost his case, then he would have to pay all the Court costs too. "It could be expensive," he said. "I don't care how much it costs," said Farmer Berg angrily, and left for home in his car.

That afternoon, Farmer Evans called to see the Lawyer, in order to take Farmer Berg to court. The Lawyer said, "I am sorry, but I am already acting for Farmer Berg, so I cannot be your Lawyer. However, I have a Lawyer-friend in the next street. I will write a letter to him for you, and he will plead your case in the court." The Lawyer wrote out a letter, to his Lawyer-friend. He sealed the letter carefully, and gave it to Farmer Evans.

Farmer Evans felt very uneasy about taking his best friend to court. So he opened the lawyer's letter, which he was not really supposed to do.

THE ASSEMBLY LEADER MAY OPEN AN ENVELOPE AT THIS POINT AND READ THE MESSAGE.

The letter read,

"My Dear Lawyer-Friend,
Two silly fat geese have come to be plucked.
You pluck one, and I will pluck the other."

Farmer Evans was very glad that he had opened the letter. He now knew, that the Lawyer thought that both farmers, in their arguments about the cars, were acting like two silly geese. Worse still, the letter meant that both the lawyers considered that the farmers were rich, and could be plucked of their money.

Farmer Evans met Farmer Berg and showed him the letter. Both farmers were sorry that they had been angry with their best friend. They both apologised to each other, saying that they were very sorry. They both put their cars into the garage to be repaired, because they had forgotten that each year, they had paid an insurance premium. This meant that the Insurance Company would pay for the repairs to both cars because it had been a genuine accident.

Next Sunday, both the Berg family and the Evans family sat together again in the long pew in the Chapel. Everyone was happy because both farmers had forgiven each other. The only thing that changed, after all the fuss, was that Farmer Berg and Farmer Evans took more care to look into their driving mirrors, when they were reversing their cars at the school house. They became more careful drivers.

Prayer:

Lord teach us to value our friends.
to forgive the mistakes of others
seventy times seven.
Save us from a foolish anger
and an unforgiving spirit.   Amen.

Hymn:

Make me a channel of your peace. (C&P. 2. 148) or (J.P. 161)

Teachers' Note: (1) To have good friends is a very great privilege. Farmer Berg and Farmer Evans had more to lose than to gain, by their silly quarrel. (2) Friends usually quarrel because of a misunderstanding. It is always necessary to view matters from the other person's point of view, as well as looking at the problem from our own view-point. (3) Jesus taught us to forgive those who offend us, seventy times seven.

(b) The Angry Footballer   *Week 5   Anger*

The School football "A" team was made up mostly from the top class. The school Sport's Teacher had built up a very good side. The players wore yellow and blue jerseys and white shorts. The "A" team was made up of four girls and seven boys. The reserve players came mostly from year five class, and they were named the "B" Team.

The two teams used to keep up practice, by playing each other on their own school playing field. They had one very good player named Geoffrey, who was a goal-scorer. However, sad to say, Geoffrey had one terrible fault. He had a bad temper. He sometimes could not control himself on the field, especially when another player from an opposing team, managed to take the ball away from him.

The Referee sometimes had to give Geoffrey a warning that he would be sent off, if he did not behave himself. The problem was that Geoffrey did not know why he would kick out at another player. "I don't know why I do it", he would say after the match, "I just feel tense and angry inside".

Kitty, was a tall Irish girl in the "A" team. She told Geoffrey that he was just a big spoilt baby. "We are not going to play with you on the field any more, if you persist in kicking other players instead of the ball. You are a good goal scorer, but your behaviour lets our school down. We are getting a bad reputation because of you." Geoffrey in himself knew that Kitty was right. He hated himself, afterwards. The other players just shook their heads, as if to say, "Why does he do it?"

Next day, Kitty was taking her little dog, Dougal, along the road for a walk, when a big Collie dog ran at him, as if it were a bully and wanted to fight smaller dogs. Kitty used her leather dog-lead to chase the bigger dog off. All that day, her little dog seemed to be in a bad mood. He snarled and growled at anyone who came near. When Kitty's Dad arrived home, she told him that Dougal had become bad tempered for some reason. Dougal even snapped at Kitty's Mum.

Dad said that Dougal somehow had been badly frightened, and being a nervous dog, he was protecting himself. Kitty said, "Dad you are right. A big Collie dog attacked Dougal this morning." Then Dad made a strange statement. "Dogs and human beings are very much alike. Give them a fright, and they will act as if they are braver than lions. They will attack even their own friends, if they feel they are being threatened. People put on a brave face, yet they may be full of fear inside."

Next day, Kitty went to school, thinking very deeply. She thought that Geoffrey had acted very like Dougal. If Geoffrey had been a dog, he would have snarled and growled on certain occasions. Kitty sat with Geoffrey at lunch time. She asked him, when they were alone, whether he ever had been badly frightened in the past. Geoffrey did not say anything for quite a long time. He just stared.

Then Geoffrey slowly told her. "When I was only seven years old, I was going to the corner shop for a pint of milk, when three bigger boys hit me, and stole my money. For a laugh, they lifted me up, and put me inside the back of an open lorry, with high sides, which had been parked outside the shop. Then they ran away.

The driver came out of a house, started the engine, and drove the lorry down the street, not knowing that I was standing crying in the back of it. At the end of the street, the driver happened to look back in his driving mirror. He saw me, and he stopped. He lifted me down from the lorry. I ran all the way home. I was terribly frightened. At night I still dream about it. I took money from my money-box to buy another pint of milk for my parents. I have never told anyone else about it. I am glad that I was able to tell you, Kitty. I feel quite relieved now."

Kitty said, "Geoffrey, you should not have kept that fearful thing inside you all those years. Now that you have told me, you can tell your parents, and tell the teacher as well." Geoffrey took Kitty's advice. He told his parents and his school teacher.

A strange thing happened to Geoffrey. He was no longer nervous, or bad tempered again. He was never known to kick out at other players on the football field after that day. He became an even better goal-scorer, because he had red himself of the fear, which for so long, he had bottled up inside himself. Everybody in the "A" and the "B" team loved him, and were proud of him.

Geoffrey made up his mind that if anything nasty ever happened to him again, that he would tell his parents and his teacher. Kitty said, to him, "Maybe, if you had said your prayers every night before you went to bed, you would have found it easier to tell your earthly parents. Saying your prayers, is just like telling your heavenly Father what has happened. I always feel better, after I say my prayers."

Prayer:

> Father of every family on earth,
> teach us to bring our worry and fears to you.
> Show us all the need to pray.
> Bless our parents and teachers,

and may we learn to trust each other.
Open our hearts, to all that is pure and good.   Amen.

Hymn:

I've got peace like a river. (C&P. 2. 143) or (J.P. 120)

Teachers' Note: (1) Geoffrey had allowed tension to build up inside himself, and then he had to release it by kicking others on the football field. (2) When we try to bury our worries and fears, it shows up in our actions when we are under pressure. (3) When Geoffrey told his worry to Kitty, and to his parents and to his teacher, he had nothing more to bury deep down inside himself. He was happy and free again. He became an even better goal-scorer. A good way to get rid of your fear is to tell God about it in prayer.

(c) Angry in Church

Temples, and Synagogues, Mosques and Churches, Chapels and Cathedrals, are all buildings in which people worship God. They are buildings which we should all respect. They are meant to be buildings of peace. If you ever go to St. Patrick's Cathedral in Dublin, Eire, look for an old wooden door, standing against a wall. Take a good look at the door, because it has a hole cut out of it, as if with an axe.

It was once the side door of the Cathedral. Long ago, two Irish land Barons had a quarrel. Each Baron had a band of soldiers, who fought against each other. Both men were very angry with each other. One of the Barons having been defeated, retreated with his soldiers inside the Cathedral, and locked the strong wooden door. The enemy Baron, thought to himself, "Why should I be fighting a fellow Irishman at this time. I will go with my soldiers to the Cathedral, and make peace with my enemy."

Of course, when he arrived outside the large building, the heavy wooden door was locked, and his enemy Baron inside, would not open it up, afraid of being killed by sword or spear. The friendly Baron outside, ordered his soldiers to cut a hole in the wooden side door of the Cathedral, since they were trying to talk to each other through a closed door. When the soldiers outside had cut a hole in the door, the friendly Baron outside, shouted through the hole, "Let us be friends again. Let us shake hands through this hole in the door." But the Baron inside was still afraid, because if he had put his hand through the hole, the enemy soldiers outside could easily have cut his arm off with a sword. So he refused to put his hand through the hole.

The Baron outside, shouted to his old enemy inside, "To show you that I mean no harm, I will put my hand through the door into the Cathedral, and you may shake me by the hand. That will be an act of friendship and faith." Then the Baron outside put his hand through the hole in the door, and both men, who had been enemies, shook hands, and became good friends. The Cathedral door was opened, and everyone became happy again. Of course, the Cathedral Ministers had to have a new wooden door made by carpenters. They left the door with the hole in it against the wall, as a reminder to everyone, that the Cathedral was the House of God, and the place of peace and worship.

Jesus had a high regard for the Jewish Temple in Jerusalem. He called it, "My Father's House." There was once a time when he became really angry. He went to the Temple, and he saw that in the outer Court, business men were exchanging money, and taking a profit for themselves. Dealers were selling, sheep, and oxen, and pigeons, also for their own gain, just as if it were a market. Jesus believed that the holy Temple was a place where people should worship God, and that it should not be used for selfish ends.

He was very displeased. He showed how angry he was, by overturning the tables of the money changers. He used a short rope as a whip, not to beat the people, but just as a farmer might do, when he was driving the cattle out. Jesus said to those who sold doves, "Get these out of here. How dare you turn my Father's house into a market, when it should be a house of prayer."

From this story we learn that Jesus had great respect for a holy building. We also learn a second thing. We may be may be angry for a good reason. Some people are angry for a wrong reason, perhaps, just because they have lost their temper. Jesus did not lose his temper that day. He was careful to control his anger. He really was trying to make the religious people think about what they were doing.

The Bible teaches us to "be slow to anger."

Prayer:

> Father God, we thank you for places of worship.
> Churches and chapels, cathedrals,
> and temples, and mosques.
> We pray that they will always be places of peace.
> Help us to control unholy anger, and bad temper.
> Above all, give us grace to forgive others.   Amen.

Hymn:

> Peace is flowing like a river. (C&P. 2. 144)

Teachers' Note: (1) Every religion shows respect for the building which they use for worship. Even though we may pray to God in the temple of our heart. (2)

Churches especially are places of peace and forgiveness. (3) Jesus was angry in a good cause, but his anger was controlled anger. We must always be slow to anger.

(a) A Breath of Fresh Air   *Week 6   Life*

One Saturday, a crowd of boys went together to play football on a beach not far from where they lived. The beach was a lovely flat sandy place. Not many people visited the beach because it lay a mile from the main road, and it was situated behind a village. Further along the beach there was a large factory near the sea, but that was the only building.

It being a lovely Summer afternoon, the boys played football on the sand, but soon they became rather hot. They stopped their game for short time, to dig a long hole in the dry sand. Gareth, just for fun, lay down in the hole, and his friends covered his feet with sand. Then they covered his legs. Next they covered his body right up to his neck with the sand. Others put sand around his head, and just left his eyes, nose and mouth to be seen. It was a very silly and dangerous thing to do, but the boys did not mean any harm.

Someone kicked the ball, and everyone jumped up to kick it, and quickly the football game started up again. Everyone for the moment forgot about Gareth, as they ran after the ball. Gareth, lying under the sand, could not move his arms. When he tried to move his head, the sand covered all his face. He lay under the sand, unable to breathe, or to call for help. Meanwhile, the football game moved a little further up the beach.

Suddenly, one of the boys remembered, and he shouted, "Boys, where is Gareth?" The whole group of boys looked at the sand, but Gareth could not be seen anywhere. Worse still, they had lost the exact place where they had buried him. They searched here and there in the sand, and it took quite a time, before the boys realised that they had followed the ball, further up the beach. They went back to where their folded coats were lying, and at last, they saw the mound of dry sand. They used their hands to push away the sand from Gareth's face, but they found that he had become unconscious. His face was a blue colour, through not breathing in fresh air with oxygen in it. Gareth was nearly dead. The boys did not know what to do.

Just at that moment, there was only one other person on the beach. Fortunately, it was the "First Aid" man from the factory, going for a short stroll on the sand. The boys ran up to him and told him what had happened. The man immediately began to run to where Gareth was lying. He looked at Gareth's blue face, then he shouted to the boys to run to the village to 'phone 999 for an ambulance. "Don't waste a minute," he shouted.

The First Aid man, quickly cleaned the sand out of Gareth's nose and mouth. He began to give Gareth the kiss of life as he carefully cleaned away the sand from his eyes. He kept blowing into Gareth's mouth, and pushing up and down with his hands on the boy's chest. In what seemed to be a short time, the ambulance came up the beach, its klaxon horn sounding loud and clear. "Baaa-Baaa, Baaa-Baaa." (Again, it was fortunate, that there was an ambulance station so near the factory.)

The Ambulance men, knew exactly what to do. They put an oxygen mask over Gareth's mouth, and they carried him, as he was breathing oxygen from a long tube, attached to a metal cylinder. The rescue party were soon in the ambulance, and the klaxon horn sounded, "Baaa-Baaa, Baaa-Baaa" as it raced for the local hospital.

The boys were rather shocked at what had happened. They felt that, perhaps, they were partly to blame. They made up their mind that never again would they bury anyone in the sand. Gareth did not die after all, but he spent some time in hospital. His mother was very worried. Gareth made up his mind that he would learn First Aid, when he was older.

The factory "First Aid" man was thankful that he had taken his stroll along the shore, just at that time. There had not been any other other person available, who could have helped in the emergency. A life had been saved because he had been trained for this kind of accident. The "First Aid man" knew that no-one could remain alive without breathing fresh air.

Have you ever thought about it? Everyone needs to breathe fresh air into their lungs. Air is a free gift from God.

Prayer:

> Heavenly Father, we thank you,
> for the sunshine, the sand, and the sea.
> We are happy to breathe in God's good fresh air.
> We thank you for clean water.
> Forgive us for our mistakes.
> Bless Ambulance men, Nurses and Doctors.   Amen.

Hymn:

> There are hundreds of sparrows, thousands, millions, (C&P. 1. 15) (J.P. 246)

Teachers' Note: (1) There are good games, and there are foolish games. Burying anyone in sand is foolish and dangerous. (2) How fortunate the boys were to have the help of a trained industrial worker in "First Aid". How fortunate they were to have an ambulance station so near to the scene of the accident. (3) We live healthy lives, by breathing God's good clean air into our lungs.

(b) Three Coach Drivers   *Week 6   Life*

I want everyone to imagine that you are called Mr. Moneybags. You have to make a decision about employing one of three men who applied for the job of your coachman. Listen carefully to the story, and then say whether Mr. Moneybags made the right choice or not. You must be able to say "Why" you think that the final choice was a good one.

During the eighteenth century, there once lived a Mr. Moneybags, who was a rich land-owner. He also owned a beautiful mansion house, situated on a high hill. The road up to the house, went along the side of a dangerous rocky cliff. There was no fence or wall at the side of the road. The road was really only a stoney track. Looking down over the cliff edge, it was possible to see the jagged rocks in the valley below.

Mr. Moneybags always felt dizzy, and nervous, as his coachman drove the coach and four horses, up or down the narrow road, along-side the dangerous cliff. One day the coachman, left his employment with the land-owner. Mr. Moneybags had to advertise for a new coachman.

Three men applied for the job. At ten o'clock on the appointed day, the three men arrived at the landowner's house. They each had to meet Mr. Moneybags personally, to discuss whether they were suitable for the job of coachman.

The first man was a friendly Mr. Nitwit, who went into the drawing room. He sat down in the chair and winked at the landowner. Mr. Moneybags said to him, "As my coachman, you would have to drive the coach and four horses alongside that dangerous cliff, with me inside the coach. How near to the cliff edge could you drive that coach?" The friendly Mr. Nitwit smiled and answered. "Well Sir, if I was very drunk, I could drive the coach and horses right to the very edge of the cliff, even in the dark without moonlight." Mr. Moneybags, trembled with fear, and decided that the friendly Mr. Nitwit would not be his next coachman. Mr. Nitwit left the room.

The second man to apply for the job, next came into the room. He was a tall dark handsome man called Mr. Dreamer. He sat down, and tugged at his beard and twiddled his moustache. Mr. Moneybags asked him the same question. "As my coachman, you would have to drive the coach and four horses alongside that dangerous cliff, with me inside the coach. How near to the edge of the cliff could you drive that coach?" The handsome Mr. Dreamer answered, "Well Sir, if I had enjoyed a goodnight's sleep, I could drive that coach and horses so near to the edge of the cliff, that your hair would stand up with fear." Mr. Moneybags trembled again, and he decided that the handsome Mr. Dreamer would not be his next coachman. Mr. Dreamer left the room.

The third man to apply for the job was a Mr. Wiseman. He had a daffodil pinned on the lapel of his jacket, and he offered the landowner a sugar bon- bon from a paper bag. Mr. Moneybags asked him the same question as he had asked the other two men. "As my coachman, you would have to drive the coach and four horses alongside that dangerous cliff, with me inside the coach. How near to the edge of the cliff could you drive that coach?" Mr. Wiseman answered, "Well Sir, if I had an ounce of commonsense in my head, I would drive that coach and horses, as far away as I could from that cliff edge." Mr. Moneybags smiled at Mr. Wiseman, and gave him the job as his coachman.

The edge of the cliff, had terrified Mr. Moneybags. He needed a coachman whom he could rely upon for every journey. He needed a coachman who would not to take any foolish risks which might cause the coach and horses to fall over the cliff edge. Life is too valuable, and we must never take silly risks that might harm ourselves, or someone else.

Prayer:

> Heavenly Father, we thank you for life itself.
> We ask that we might use the hours wisely.
> Save us from taking foolish risks,
> or leading others into danger.
> Show us that it is better to keep as far away
> as we can from any wrong doing.
> Through Jesus Christ our Lord.   Amen.

Hymn:

> We thank you Lord for all we eat. (C&P. 2. 136)

Teachers' Note: (1) The point of this story is that we might keep as far away from danger, or wrong doing as we can. (2) Mr. Wiseman was only wise because he refused to take foolish risks with life and limb. (3) Life is a free gift from God to each one of us. How we spend it depends largely on our personal choices.

(c) David Spares Saul's Life   *Week 6   Life*

After David killed Goliath, the tall Philistine soldier, he was treated like a hero. He had honour among King Saul's soldiers. However, Saul was a very jealous man. He did not like anyone to receive more praise than himself. When David returned from the war, he had to pass some of the cities of Israel. As he was passing, women in crowds, came out of to see him going by with the army. The women began to sing,

"Saul has killed thousands of his enemies,
but David has killed tens of thousands."

This song meant that David was ten times a better soldier than King Saul. David's popularity made King Saul very jealous indeed. The very next day, David was playing his harp for the King. Saul often went into a bad mood. This time, King Saul felt hatred for David even more than before. He picked up a javelin, and threw it at David intending to kill him. David jumped to the one side and the javelin missed him, and pierced the wall behind. David quickly escaped from the room.

Some time afterwards, David fell in love with Michal, the King's daughter and they were married. Saul secretly told Jonathan, his son, to kill David. However, Jonathan privately warned David, "My father, the King wants to kill you. I advise you to get away and hide somewhere." Soon David and Jonathan became very good friends. King Saul threw a javelin at David a second time, but again David moved quickly, and the javelin missed him.

After the second attempt on his life, David had to go into hiding. Jonathan arranged, that he would give David a signal, as to whether it was safe or not for him to return. Next day, Jonathan took his bow and arrow, and shot his arrow beyond the target. This was the pre-arranged signal, to warn David to escape, because his life was in danger.

King Saul, with his soldiers, was searching for David with the intention of killing him. The soldiers that evening set up their camp. They put the King's royal tent in the middle of the camp, with the soldiers' tents surrounding the King's tent. This arrangement was designed to keep the King safe. General Abner, commander of Saul's army, slept in the royal tent. He was also present there to guard the King.

That night in the darkness, David crept up to the camp. He quietly came past the tents of the sleeping soldiers. Then even more carefully, he entered the royal tent, where King Saul was sleeping. General Abner was also asleep. David took the jug of water from the side of Saul's pillow. He also took Saul's spear. David slipped away into the darkness, and escaped into the night.

Next day, David stood on a hill-top, far off from the camp, but in a high place where people in the camp below could hear him. He shouted down to the soldiers, "Why have you not protected your King. Look, here is the King's jug of water, that was beside his pillow, and here is his spear." King Saul heard the voice shouting down to the camp. He knew that the voice belonged to David. He called out, "Is that your voice, I hear, David?"

David shouted back, "Yes, it is my voice. I have done nothing wrong. Why does my King want to kill me?" King Saul realised that David could easily have killed him in the darkness, when everyone was asleep. Yet, David had spared his life. Saul realised that he had been acting very foolishly. He shouted, "I admit that I have done wrong to you. I never again will do you any harm, because you have spared my life." Once more, King Saul and David became friends and trusted each other. Saul went back to his royal palace.

Prayer:

Heavenly Father, you are the Lord of life.
You are the Lord of time.
Teach us, that when we have quarrels,
to forgive each other.
Give us all the ability to work with each other.
Give us the patience to understand each other.   Amen.

Hymn:

Morning has broken. (C&P. 1. 1) or (J.P. 166)

Teachers' Note: (1) Saul was jealous of David because people admired him. Jealousy is unnecessary because everyone has individual gifts. (2) David found his wife, Michal, in Saul's family. His best friend was Jonathan, who was King Saul's son. David must have had a pleasant personality. (3) David could have taken revenge and killed Saul, but he never did. It takes two to make an argument! We all can forgive our enemies, if we try. God forgives us if we ask him.

(a) The Forgotten Pancakes   *Week 7   Lent*

THE ASSEMBLY LEADER, MAY LIKE TO USE A FRYING PAN CONTAINING A LARGE, FRESHLY COOKED (COOL) PANCAKE IN ORDER TO ILLUSTRATE THE DIFFICULT ART OF TOSSING A PANCAKE.

The football team at the Junior school decided to have a real pancake race on "Pancake Tuesday" afternoon. The members of the football team had arranged that each member had to bring a frying pan from their own home to the school. The P.E. Teacher had said that the frying pans had to be thoroughly washed in detergent beforehand. He said that he would send home any pupil who brought a greasy pan.

Every member of the football team, including the reserves, was allowed to take part in the Pancake Race. The race was to be held around the outside of the football field. Any runner who went over the marked line was to be disqualified.

Every ten steps, the runners had to toss their pancakes once in the air, and catch them again in their frying pans. If the pancake fell on the ground, then the runner was disqualified, so everyone had to practise carefully beforehand.

A brand new stainless steel frying pan full of chocolate Easter Eggs packed in cellophane paper was to be the First Prize. A box of chocolates was the Second Prize. A large stick of Pink Seaside Rock was to be the Third Prize. The P.E. Teacher jokingly had said, that if anyone did not like chocolate, then that runner could try to come in third place. The children all laughed at the wise-crack, except those who did not see the funny side of coming in third. The Sports Teacher said that the children could eat the pancakes after the race, only if they had not fallen on the ground.

On Pancake Tuesday morning, the members of the football team and the reserves arrived at school, each one carrying a frying pan. Some were rather large pans, and others were of smaller size. The competitors had to write their names on the frying pans, so that no-one would take home the wrong pan. About eleven O'clock the P.E. Teacher came rushing into the Staff Room. He looked very worried. He blurted out, "What can I do? I have been so keen to organise the race, that I have forgotten to ask anyone to make the pancakes. You cannot have a pancake race without pancakes." Everyone looked at each other in dismay. The P.E. Teacher said that he felt very silly indeed.

Helen was one of the older girls, and she had just called at the staff room to collect her tartan scarf, which she had left behind the previous day. She heard what the P.E. Teacher had said. Helen suggested, "Why not ask the dinner ladies to make up two big jugs of pancake batter during the Lunch break. There are plenty of metal dinner trays in the Dining Hall. The metal trays could be heated, on the school gas cookers, and the pancake batter could be poured on to the hot trays. We could help the Dinner Ladies to make about thirty pancakes before two o'clock this afternoon." The P. E. Teacher thought that it was a grand idea, and the other Teachers nodded in agreement.

Needless to say, the Dinner Ladies were delighted to make the pancake batter. Three of the older girls helped to make forty-five lovely tasty pancakes. (Fifteen more than they expected to make!) All the pupils were allowed out of class, to watch the Pancake Tuesday Race. A girl gained the First Prize, and two boys gained the Second, and Third Prizes. Fourteen of the competitors accidently dropped their pancakes on the grass, and they were disqualified. Everyone trooped back into the Assembly Hall.

The Vicar was there to explain why the day was a special one. He said that Pancake Tuesday, really should be called "Shrove Tuesday". It was the day before "Ash Wednesday," which was the beginning of "Lent" in the Church calender. Lent lasted for six weeks. Lent meant "Spring-Time." The practice of making pancakes was an old custom. Church members were not supposed to eat rich food during Lent because it was a time of "Fasting." Abstaining from food helped people to discipline (rule) themselves, just as athletes, such as runners give up smoking or over-eating.

Pan-cakes were cheap food, and easily made even by very poor people, who could clear out their cupboard, and use up their old flour, butter, and milk. It became the custom at the beginning of Lent, to eat these cakes, which are made so quickly in the pan. Pancakes had to be tossed over, after one side had been baked. The Vicar said that this was why pancakes were tossed in the race. Lent also celebrated the time when the Lord Jesus fasted for forty days in the wilderness. The children were all invited to attend Church the following Sunday. When the Vicar sat down again, the pupils knew that the school day was over. They now understood what the old custom meant.

The children thought that Pancake Tuesday was a "super" kind of day. They could hardly bear to wait to get home from school. They guessed what kind of baking would be freshly made by their Mums or Grans, and what would be set on the plate on the table at "Tea-time." They looked forward to next year's Pancake Race.

Prayer:

> Father God, we thank you for Shrove Tuesday.
> We thank you for the six weeks of Lent, before Easter,
> when we may specially remember our Lord Jesus.
> Teach us to understand, that his temptation,
> his death, and his resurrection,
> happened for our learning.   Amen.

Hymn:

> Praise the Lord in the rhythm of your music. (C&P. 1. 33)

Teachers' Note: (1) Sometimes the most important factors are forgotten. The Sports Teacher forgot to supply the pancakes for the race. (2) The speed with with the pancakes were actually made, is a modern illustration of why pancakes were originally chosen, (to leave more time for spiritual exercises). (3) Self -rule (discipline) is good for all of us. Jesus ruled himself, when fasting in the wilderness.

(b) The Jig-Saw Puzzle   *Week 7   Lent*

There was a factory, which made jig-saw puzzles. Mrs. Evans pasted a beautiful picture on a flat piece of plywood, and Mr. Garth, put the the wood-backed picture into a machine. The machine had many little wood saws attached to it. When it was switched on, the machine cut out the jig-saw shapes. A teenage boy, called Tony, at the other end of the machine, packed the pieces into a coloured box. The jig-saw puzzles were now ready for the delivery van to take them to the shops.

One day, the factory was making really difficult jig-saw puzzles. The picture showed a map of the world. However, Tony thought that he would like to do Mrs. Evans' job for a little while. So he picked up a flat piece of plywood upside down, and he pasted a map of the world on it. He did not know that the Mrs. Evans had already pasted a picture of a man and a woman, and a boy and a girl on the other side. Because the picture was underneath, Tony did not see it, as he passed the plywood to Garth.

Soon, Mr. Garth had put the plywood into the machine, and when the pieces had been sawn, they came out the otherside. Tony ran round to the other side of the machine. He lifted all the hundreds of pieces, and put them into a cardboard box. Soon the cardboard boxes were put into an even bigger box, ready for the delivery lorry to take away to the shops.

A month passed by, and the jig-saw puzzles had been sold to customers. In one school, it happened that two teachers were ill, and no other teachers could be found to take one of the classes. The Headteacher, came into the class that was without a Teacher.

He said to the class, "Now children, I cannot find a teacher to take your class today, so I am asking you to do a very difficult thing. I have an expensive jig-saw puzzle here. It is a picture of a map of the world. I want you all to get around the large table, and to spend all day in fitting the pieces together. I know that this is the most difficult jig-saw that you have ever done. None of you are very good at geography." The Headteacher went away, chuckling. "That will keep them quiet until half-past- three this afternoon," he thought to himself.

The children in the class felt strange, being left alone on their best behaviour. They all sat round a large long table, and began to put the jig-saw pieces together. They worked together for half an hour, but not being very good at maps, they did not get very far.

Then one of the girls shouted out, as she turned the jig-saw piece over, "Look, everybody, I have a blue eye on my piece. I think that there are two sides to this jig-saw puzzle." The children looked very closely at their pieces. Eventually, they discovered that the picture on the back was a picture of four people. They all agreed that it would be easier to fit pieces together showing people rather than maps.

Every person in the class worked as fast as they could. Soon the picture was finished. Then they put the jig saw on top of a very large tray. They put another tray on top of the jig-saw, in order to hold it flat. Then, still holding on tightly, they carefully turned the two trays upside down. When they removed the top tray, there lay a map of the world. They all gave three cheers. Only one hour had passed.

The other Teachers came running in to see what had happened. They were amazed that the class had put together a difficult map of the world in such a short time. The children all kept the secret. The Teachers asked the children, "Please, tell us how you finished the puzzle so quickly?" One boy stood up, and said, "We found out that if you get the people right, then you get the world right!"

The Teachers smiled, and they were pleased that their pupils were so clever. Tony the factory worker never knew how he had accidentally put two pictures on the one jig-saw.

Many newspapers and the television news programmes report that the world is not right. There are stories and pictures of wars, and bank robberies, and violent actions. The world looks to be full of hunger, and sadness, and wrong doing. The question for us in the Assembly today is, "How can the world be made right? The answer is that if we begin with people, the world will turn out all right. If we are kind to all people, feed the hungry people, care for sick people, protect weak people, and love all children, then the rest of the world will become a better place to live in.'

Individual children are important, because in twenty years time, they will be the engineers, television stars, bus drivers, seamen, nurses, shop-keepers, taxi-drivers, doctors, ministers, footballers, priests, teachers, pilots, musicians and members of parliament. To make the future world right, you must begin with making people right. If we pray, God can help us to make the world right. The period of Lent is a special time to pray to God.

Prayer:

Heavenly Father, we thank you for our world.
It is a beautiful place of hills and valleys.
The green fields, hedges, and the seaside,
all make us feel happy.
We pray that people will cease from wrong-doing.
For we know that when people become better people,
the world will be a better world.   Amen.

Hymn:

O Lord all the world belongs to you. (C&P. 1. 39)

Teachers' Note: (1) The story began with Tony accidentally putting two pictures on the one jig-saw puzzle. Good can come out of even an accident. (2) The class were working together on the one project as a team. This is good for people, young or old. They discovered a faster method of completing the puzzle. (3) This is like a parable story. Get people right, and you make the world right.

(c) **The Big Pearl**

There was once a pearl fisher called Ruben, whose life work, was diving down into the deep blue waters of the Persian Gulf, searching for pearls. In those far off days there were no oxygen masks joined by a tube to oxygen cylinders. Oxygen breathing apparatus had not yet been invented. A pearl fisher had to learn to hold his breath for a long time, as he searched for oysters. along the bed of the sea. The pearl fisher under the sea, would reach a point, when his lungs felt as if they were bursting, and at that point, he would quickly return to the surface for a breath of fresh air.

Ruben, being a good pearl fisher, in the past, had brought up many hundreds of oysters. He had found hundreds of small pearls inside the oysters over the years that he had been swimming. Most of the oyster shells had not any pearls inside them. Every pearl fisher dreamed of one day finding a really large pearl, that could be sold for a lot of money.

A pearl is caused when a tiny grain of sand gets inside the shell of the oyster. The grain of sand causes irritation in the flesh of the oyster. The oyster sheds a tear over the grain of sand. The tear hardens like plastic around the tiny grain of sand. The more often the sand inside irritates the oyster, the more often the oyster will shed another tear, which again, will harden. A tiny pearl, grows larger over time. Kings and Queens will wear pearls in their crowns. Rich ladies will wear a string of real pearls around their neck.

Ruben, the pearl fisher, one day brought up an oyster shell. He threw it into his little boat, and climbed in after it. He took his knife, and prised open the oyster shell. He could not believe his eyes. There inside was the largest pearl that he had ever seen. He took out the big pearl, and brought it to a Merchant who was a Dealer in precious stones. (Today, we might call him a "Jeweller.") The Merchant gave Ruben a lot of money for the big pearl, and Ruben did not need to work so hard after that. The Merchants usually sold their pearls to other Merchants for even more money.

That is not the end of the story. It is really the beginning of a parable that Jesus told to his disciples. Jesus said that the Kingdom of Heaven is like a pearl. He told the story of a merchant who loved the beauty and value of pearls. He became a Dealer in pearls. He travelled the world, hoping that he might one day find a pearl, that would be so big, and worth so much money that he would be richer than anyone else.

One day, the Merchant travelled to a city, and there he was shown the biggest pearl that he had ever seen. (Who knows, it might have been the pearl originally found by Ruben.) The Merchant asked the price of the magnificent pearl. It was very costly indeed. The Merchant went home, and sold everything that he owned.

He sold his house, his farm, and all his other stock of pearls. When he had collected all his money, he went to the City Dealer, and bought the biggest and most valuable pearl in the world. It was a beauty! Now the Merchant felt he was a happy man. He now possessed such a valuable pearl, that any King or Queen would give almost anything, to own it. The Merchant felt that he was the richest man in all the world.

The story means that the Kingdom of Heaven is like the pearl. It is worth giving up everything else to possess it. The Kingdom of Heaven is God's rule inside us. It is a name for the peace and joy of believing in Jesus Christ. Many rich people are not really happy. During the period of Lent, we may give up something that we like, just to show that we can control our appetites and desires. Could you give up watching television for one hour a day, and try to do something useful for someone else?

The story also means that Jesus is really the Christian's pearl of greatest price. Christians think that the service of Jesus is something for which, it is worth giving up every thing else, if called upon to do so. Long ago, many Christian people became known as "Martyrs", (witnesses) because they had been condemned to die for their faith. in Jesus. They gave up their lives, and were killed by lions in the Roman Arena. When they said "Jesus is Lord," they meant that for them, Jesus was God's most precious gift to the world.

Prayer:

> Lord of all goodness,
> we thank you for the parables of Jesus.
> Guide us to an understanding
> of what is most valuable in our daily lives.
> Show us all that faith in Jesus,
> is the most valuable experience of all.
> Bless all children who need our prayers.   Amen.

Hymn:

> I'll bring to you the best gift I can offer. (C&P. 1. 59)

Teachers' Note: (1) Pearls are discovered at great risk, by deep diving fishermen. (2) Jesus told the parable, to show us that one thing is more valuable than anything else. He called it the "Kingdom of Heaven", (or the Kingdom of God,) which means "God's rule within his people". (3) For Christians, Jesus is the pearl of greatest price. Reference, Matthew 13 verses 45-46.

(a) Troon, "Ballast Bank"

Every ship that sails across the oceans of the world, usually carries some kind of cargo. It may be crockery from China, or tea from India, or machinery from Britain, or oil from Burma, or timber from Canada. There is always a danger that the cargo may be too heavy. When the cargo is too heavy, then the ship will lie low in the water. In a storm, the waves will blow over the ship, and if the ship lies too low, then the ship will sink.

If you take a look at the great iron ships that sail the seas nowadays, you will see a white line painted across a white circle on the side of the ship. This is called "The Plimsoll line." It is named after its inventor, Samuel Plimsoll. When the cargo is being loaded in the harbour, care must be taken that the ship must not be loaded so full, that the Plimsoll line goes below the water line. In this way, ships do not carry too heavy burdens in them. (There are other lines also painted on the side of the ship, such as the level for Summer, and Winter, and for fresh water and salt -water).

In the days before there were steam driven ships, or ships with oil burning engines, ships were driven by the wind. They had great sails. These ships also carried cargoes around the world. However, there was another problem, what if the cargo was too light, or if the ship was empty? When a storm arose, the empty ship would be too high in the water, and the wind would blow it on to the rocks, or else it might be blown right over on its side. The ship would soon sink. So you can see that there was a need for a Plimsoll line to be painted on every ship, to prevent underloading.

Before the Plimsoll line was painted on ships, Captains of ships had to decide what to use as ballast (weight) for their return journey. If there was a return cargo, then its weight would make the ship steady as it sailed in the sea. If there was no return cargo, then some kind of ballast was needed in place of the cargo.

Can you imagine the very first ship which sailed full of coal, from Troon, the beautiful little seaside town in Ayrshire. The sailing ship sailed across the Irish sea, to Larne harbour. The Captain's wife and little son, Alex, were also on board the ship. The journey to Ireland took only one day, if the wind was favourable. The crew unloaded the cargo of coal on the Irish quayside. The Captain's wife and his son Alex, went for a walk around the old town of Larne.

When they arrived back to the coal-ship, it had discharged its cargo. The Captain said to his wife and son, "I have a problem. I have no cargo to carry back to Troon, so the ship, will sail too high in the water. I need ballast (weight)." Little Alex thought to himself, "I must help my Father to solve his problem. What is the cheapest cargo in Ireland?"

He thought for a while, and then the answer came to him. "The cheapest cargo in Ireland was the soil in the fields." Alex said to his father, the Captain, "Dad, if a horse and cart could leave loads of soil from the fields on the Larne quayside, then every ship going back to Troon for more coal, could return with a load of soil in the ship's hold."

" What a splendid idea! " the Captain said.

From that day onwards, every ship carrying coal to Ireland, brought back a cargo of good Irish soil. They dumped the soil on the beautiful shore at Troon, in Scotland. If you ever visit Troon, which is one of the loveliest and cleanest seaside towns in Scotland, ask someone to show you the "Ballast Bank." It is a very long, high, hill covered in grass, beside the sea. The Ballast Bank is really a little bit of Ireland, carried over the Irish Sea and put down beside Troon harbour.

The burden of soil in the hold of a ship, kept it steady in the waves. Sometimes children have to carry an extra burden in life. Many children have Asthma, and have to carry an inhaler. Some children have to wear glasses. Others have to wear a hearing aid to help their hearing. Older people sometimes have to carry a walking stick, in case they fall.

Soldiers on the march have to carry an Army Pack. Mountain climbers have to carry equipment on their backs. The Plumber has to carry his tool box. The Nurse and the Doctor have to carry their little black bags. The Referee has to carry his note-book, a pencil, his whistle, and some red and some yellow cards. Your Teacher sometimes has to carry your school work back home to correct it.

Everyone has some burden to carry in life. Carrying a burden must not depress us. Sometimes we call burdens "handicaps." Remember that carrying a burden may give us inner strength. Jesus told his disciples that if they met a Roman soldier, and that soldier compelled them to carry his pack for one mile, then they should carry his pack a second mile, without being ordered to do so. This was to show the soldier goodwill.

Prayer:

Heavenly Father, we thank you,
for all those brave people,
who sail the seas in ships.
We thank you for the smaller ships
which provide people with recreation.
May our handicaps in life not depress us.
Rather, may they give us inner strength.   Amen.

Hymn:

In the morning early, I go down to the sea (C&P 1 60)

Teachers' Note: (1) Ballast is the weight inside a ship that keeps it steady in the windy sea. Handicaps need not depress us. They can give us a sense of direction in life.

(2) Not many children will see much coal nowadays, therefore it may be necessary to explain. In the past, gas was taken from coal dug up in Scotland and England. The coal was burned, to provide heat and energy. The reason the coal boats went daily to Ireland, was that there was very little coal to be found in Ireland. (Nowadays, they use Natural Gas from under the sea.).

(3) Troon still has its lovely harbour, and children in Troon love to walk on the Ballast Bank.

(b) Tommy the Table   *Week 8   Burdens*

Tommy was a school table. He was more of a nuisance or a burden than useful as a table. When the new school opened twenty years ago, Tommy arrived with all the other tables. However, he was a different size and shape from the other tables in the school. He was larger than the children's tables, and he was smaller than the Teachers' tables. No-one quite knew where to put Tommy, or what to do with him.

Tommy was used for all sorts of duties. People put their books on him. Lost property was dumped on top of him. Children sat on top of him and during the school play at Christmas time, they even stood on top of him. At the Harvest Festival at the school, a lot of vegetables in plastic bags were piled on his surface.

No-one knew exactly where the table should be put. Sometimes he was in the main hall. At other times he was in the store room, or in the corridor. As twenty years passed by, new children, and new Teachers joined the school, Tommy the table felt that he was of no real use to anybody. He realised that he was slowly being edged out of the school, because he was a different table from all the other tables. Finally, he ended up on the Caretaker's work-shed, right beside the door to the back-yard at the school. Tommy felt sure that the next stop would be the rubbish lorry. Soon, he would be thrown on the tip, where the contents of everyone's wheelie bins were dumped. Tommy felt very sorry for himself.

Mr. Bell the Headteacher, was rushing along the school corridor one day, when he saw Tommy, now a very old, dirty, disused table, lying in the caretaker's workshop. He thought to himself, "What a dilapidated old table, but it has been made of beautiful teak wood. Perhaps, one of the children's parents could brighten it up a bit. It looks a mess. I really need a special table to focus everyone's attention upon, when I am speaking at the Assembly." Tommy the table thought to himself, "Who would want an old table like me?"

The Headteacher asked the children whether any of their parents might be a wood-worker, or perhaps, even a cabinet-maker? One of the girls came back to school next day, and said that her Dad was willing to renovate the old table, if the Headteacher would suggest how he would like it. So, Tommy was carried out of the back door of the school, and down to a shed, behind a house in the next street.

In about one month's time, Tommy arrived back in school. No one would have recognised Tommy. He had his legs shortened. He had been cleaned up, and French-polished, until his beautiful teak-wood surface shone like the tables in the Queen's palace. Now, he really looked to be a magnificent table. The Headteacher placed, what looked like a brand new table, before the Assembly. He rested his books upon it. He also placed a vase of flowers on top of it, and anything else he needed specially for his talks to the children.

Tommy the table had become a special table, from that day onwards. Teachers treated him with care. The cleaning ladies loved to polish him with furniture polish, until he looked perfect. Tommy thought to himself, at last I am really a beautiful and useful piece of furniture. I am no longer a burden to the school.

Some people think that they are a burden to society around them. Yet everyone has something very useful and beautiful about them. It may be their looks, or their poise, (walk) or their charming manner, or their smile, or their singing voice, or their artistic gifts, or their helpful skills, or ability at sport, or something deep down inside them, which is called "personality." These are the personal gifts that belong to each one of us, and they show us that every child is important. No-one should ever feel that they are just a burden to others.

Prayer:

> Father God, you made us all, just as we are.
> We thank you for ourselves, and our personal gifts.
> May no-one ever feel unwanted.
> Teach us to use our personalities to make
> our world a better and a happier place.
> Show us how to become useful.   Amen.

Hymn:

> Carpenter, Carpenter, make me a tree. (C&P. 1. 5)

Teachers' Note: (1) Tommy the table was different from the other tables. (2) Tommy the table felt that he was not of any use to the school. (3) Tommy turned out to be made of beautiful teak wood, and when cleaned and polished, he found a place of honour at the school. All children in God's eyes are useful, although they may not always think that they are.

(c) **Joseph and His Family**

Joseph had become the second most powerful Ruler in Egypt. Yet he carried a secret burden inside him. He loved his old father, and his eleven brothers, but he had not seen them for many years. They lived far away in Canaan. Most of his brothers were grown men. Because Joseph had been the second youngest member of the family, he was specially fond of Benjamin, whom had been the youngest. Both boys had been playmates together.

During the famine, ten men came down from Canaan to Egypt to buy corn. There was a food shortage in Canaan. The rumour was that a wise Egyptian had stored up corn and wheat in storehouses, during seven years of plenty. Then, when the seven years of famine occurred, this wise Egyptian had ordered that the storehouses should be opened up, and grain sold to the people. The ten men had come to buy the corn, but Joseph had recognised them as his ten brothers.

Joseph remembered how they had become very jealous of him, when he lived with his father in Canaan. They were especially angry, when their father, Jacob, gave a beautiful coat of many colours to Joseph. So they captured Joseph, and threw him into a pit. Later, they sold him as a slave to passing merchants who were riding on camels. When these travelling merchants arrived in Egypt, they in turn sold Joseph as a slave. However, God had been with Joseph, and helped Joseph, even though he began as a slave, to become King Pharaoh's chief Governor.

Joseph, that day recognised his ten brothers, but they did not recognise him. The day when they had captured Joseph, they had killed a young goat, and stained Joseph's beautiful coat of many colours with its blood. They had brought the coat back to Jacob, their father, and told him that a wild beast must have killed Joseph, and that they had found his coat. Jacob was heart broken to hear such news. Everyone believed that Joseph was dead.

Joseph decided to give his brothers a fright. He accused them of being spies in Egypt. Joseph had many soldiers at his command. His brothers were very much afraid of this powerful Egyptian ruler. Joseph said, "You must send one of your company to bring your youngest brother, Benjamin, here to me, then I shall know that you are telling the truth." He kept them under guard for three days.

All the time, Joseph was making up a plan, so that he could again see Benjamin. Joseph said to his ten brothers, "I will keep one of you, Simeon, here in prison, in Egypt, and the other nine of you may go home with the bags of corn and wheat. You must bring Benjamin to me, when you come back again. Only then, can I set Simeon free."

Now all this time, Joseph was talking with his brothers through an Egyptian Interpreter. He was pretending that he did not know their language. Big tears were beginning to come into his eyes, so he turned away from his brothers, so that they would not see how much he loved them.

Secretly, Joseph told his servants to put the money which they had paid for the corn and wheat, back inside the top of their bags. The nine brothers travelled homewards. On the way homewards, they found their money in the top of their bags of grain. They came home to their father, Jacob, and told him everything that had happened.

When the family had used up the corn and the wheat, which they had brought from Egypt, they knew that they would have to return to buy more. Jacob at first, did not want to trust the brothers with taking Benjamin to Egypt. In the end, he had to agree, and Benjamin went along with the brothers. They travelled down to Egypt. They took double the money with them to pay the storehouse keeper. They also brought presents for the great Ruler of Egypt.

When Joseph saw that Benjamin, his younger brother, was with his brothers, he invited them all into his own house for a splendid feast. He also brought Simon out of prison to them. As they were enjoying the delicious food, Joseph again looked at Benjamin, who had been his little brother. This time, a lump of sadness was gathering in his throat. He had to leave the room, and went into another room.

There he cried, and cried again, because he loved Benjamin. He quickly washed his face, and returned to the dining room. Joseph himself, quickly arranged that his brothers were placed in order, from the eldest to the youngest at the table. How Joseph could know such a thing, really mystified the brothers.

After they had bought more bags of corn and wheat, the brothers left for home. Joseph, secretly, again, had told his servants to put the money in the top of the bags of grain. He also had told them to put his silver cup in the top of Benjamin's bag. Joseph sent his Steward and his soldiers in pursuit of the brothers. They soon caught up with them.

The Soldiers began to search the bags, beginning at the eldest. They searched all the brothers' bags, right down to the bag belonging to the youngest. Of course, they found the money, and in Benjamin's bag they found Joseph's own silver cup. The Steward and soldiers brought the brothers back to Joseph's palace.

The brothers were terrified, as they stood before the Egyptian Ruler. Joseph gathered the men around him, and again, tears began to come. He said to the ten brothers, "Look at me closely! I am Joseph your brother, whom you sold as a slave into Egypt. In those days, you thought that you were doing me harm, when all the time, God was changing everything into good for me. I have been able to save both my own family, and all the people of Egypt from starvation, during these seven years of famine."

Pharaoh, the King, had heard what Joseph had said to his brothers. He commanded Joseph's brothers, "Take wagons and bring your old father, Jacob, and all your household, back here to Egypt. I will give your family the best of my land, and you may all live here in happiness." Joseph sent presents with his brothers to his father.

When Jacob heard what had happened, he could hardly believe that Joseph was alive. The family travelled down to Egypt again. When Jacob and Joseph met, they hugged each other. All the family lived happily together, and they were never hungry again. God had prospered Joseph, so that Joseph could help his family, even though his brothers once had hated him. He freely forgave them.

Prayer:

Father God, we are all members of your family.
May we never injure anyone.
Teach us never to be jealous of others.
Keep us from ever wanting revenge.
May we become more like Joseph who forgave,
those who did wrong to him.   Amen.

Hymn:

Come my brothers, praise the Lord, allelujah. (C&P. 1. 20)
or (Come my sisters, praise the Lord, at last verse!)

Teachers' Note: (1) Jacob, the father, showed that Joseph was his favourite son, by giving him the coat of many colours. This was wrong. Parents should have no favourite children. They should love them all the same. (2) Joseph had no thoughts of revenge in his heart against his brothers, even though they had tried to kill him. (3) God turned evil into good, by blessing Joseph, even though a slave, he later became the famous Egyptian Governor.

(a) The Dog That Went Blind   *Week 9   Memories*

There was once a family that decided that they would love to buy a puppy. They thought that a Yellow Labrador would be an excellent breed of dog to buy. Mr. and Mrs. Bell looked up the newspapers, searching the columns of the Dog-Breeding section. The found the address of a Dog-Breeder, and off they went in the car, intending to buy the best dog they could find.

When they arrived at the Dog Breeders home, the lady was very nice to Mr. and Mrs. Bell. She told them that one of the Yellow Labrador bitches had recently had a litter of large healthy pups. She had already sold them all, except one pup. The Lady looked at Mr. and Mrs. Bell, and said to them, "There is one pup which has not yet been sold. No-one has chosen her, because she was the 'runt' of the litter. This means that she was the smallest of the seven puppies.

I want to keep this dog for myself. She may have been smaller than the other pups, but she is a very beautiful pup, nevertheless. This little pup has a lovely kind nature, and she is something special." When Mr. and Mrs. Bell first saw the little pup, they fell in love with her, immediately. They decided to buy her. The Lady made them promise that if they grew tired of the pup, that they were to bring it back.

The pup grew up into a really beautiful bitch, along with Stewart and Fiona, the two children in the house. They decided to name the dog, "Nuala." She was not really very small after all, but rather strong in build, and she was never afraid of other dogs. Best of all she had a friendly nature, and every member of the family grew to love her.

When she was a little pup, sometimes she was naughty. She chewed the children's slippers. She chewed the wooden legs of the chairs. She stole chocolate left on the table, and gobbled up the paper as well. She jumped out of the car window, when the car stopped at the traffic lights, and gave everyone such a fright. When she grew older, she gobbled up one pound of pork sausages from the kitchen table, before they could be put into the refrigerator. She could easily smell sweets in anyone's pockets. She used to chase the cats out of the garden. Everyone forgave Nuala her naughty pranks because she was such a beautiful and lovable dog.

She loved to go with the family to the Lake District. She would swim far out into the lake, to retrieve sticks which had been thrown. Nuala would then swim back to the shore in a great circle. When she went to the seaside, Nuala was always first into the sea. At night time, she would slip up to the bedroom in the darkness, and sleep at the foot of the bed. Then, when morning light came, she went around the beds, waking the family up. She could catch any ball that the children threw, and she had such good scenting skills, that she could find any ball that was lost.

As Nuala grew to be about ten years old, the children noticed that she was missing finding the ball sometimes. This was especially, when they threw it a long way, or into the long grass. A few days later, the vet told the family the sad news that Nuala was going blind. Soon the family pet could not see. This made the Bell family care for their dog even more. Even though Nuala was blind, she was still a faithful pet. She really did not need her eyes, since she could smell her way about. When the children were outside, they kept her on a lead more often. They loved Nuala more than anything else they owned.

One day a black and white she-kitten arrived to live with the Bell family. They called her "Holly." Mr. and Mrs. Bell, Stewart, and Fiona, wondered how Nuala and the new kitten would get on together. No one need have worried, because both animals became the best of friends. Although Nuala could not see the kitten, she could smell her presence. The cat always cuddled up close to Nuala, and both went to sleep together. Maybe, Nuala thought that the kitten was another little puppy, come to be her special friend, because she was blind. The lively kitten and the blind dog loved each other very much.

Nuala reached the age of fifteen years, which is very old for a dog. Then one day, she felt very tired. She lay down to sleep on the best settee, and quietly died in her sleep. Everyone at home cried. The kitten, of course, did not understand what had happened. She would scamper though the rooms looking for her doggie friend.

Mr. Bell dug her grave in a lovely part of the garden, under some young trees. A little headstone with the name "Nuala" stands at the head of her grave. Lovely flowers are always growing on top of the grave. Even though Nuala was dead and gone, her memory made everyone feel good and kind. The Bell family thanked God that they had the opportunity of enjoying the friendship of such a wonderful dog.

Prayer:

> Father, we are all part of your family.
> May we all be good friends.
> May we always be kind to animals.
> We thank you for our own homes,
> and our parents who take care of us.
> Bless our school, our lessons, and our Teachers.   Amen.

Hymn:

> All the animals that I have ever seen. (C&P. 2. 80)

Teachers' Note: In what three ways is Nuala like school children? (1) Nuala may have been the smallest pup in the litter, but she grew up to be a very beautiful dog. Life always brings surprising changes. (2) Nuala was mischievous sometimes, but she was also full of love and friendship. (3) Nuala had a little kitten-friend, "Holly," who helped to keep her happy in her blindness. We all may make friends with someone else.

(b) Fire

Week 9   Memories

"Remember, remember, the Fifth of November!" Do you remember the last time you saw a bonfire? Here are five qualities of a bonfire.

(A)   *Fire attracts attention.* In the sixteenth century, there were no telephones, or radios to pass on a warning, if enemy ships were going to attack our island home. Instead, beacon fires were built on high places, many miles apart. These beacons were piles of dry wood set in an iron basket, on top of an iron pole. If an enemy fleet of warships were sailing to attack London, or an enemy army was marching through the country, the enemy might have be seen far away on the North East coast of England. One beacon fire would be set alight on top of a hill, and twenty miles away, someone would see the fire burning, and they would also light their beacon fire, and maybe it would be seen fifty miles away. They in turn would light a third beacon fire. In a short time, a long chain of fires would burn across the country, warning the people in far away London, that enemy ships, or an enemy army were going to attack them. The chain of fires across England was successful, because fire attracts attention

(B)   *Fire destroys.* In 1664-65 there was once a great epidemic, named the "Black Plague." People died in thousands. The germs of the Plague were spread by fleas, which lived on the backs of rats, which came out of the London sewers. Then, in 1665, there was a fire, which began in at a bakers' shop in Pudding Lane. Most of the streets of London were very narrow, and the wooden houses were built close together.

The wind blew and spread the flames. Not only was the Bakers' shop destroyed, but most of the old London wooden houses caught fire, and they were burned to the ground. After the Great Fire was finally put out, a strange thing happened. People stopped dying from the Black Plague sickness. Soon it was realised that the Great Fire of London had not only destroyed the houses, but it had also destroyed the Plague germs. The Fire of London turned out to be a blessing in disguise. The disease was gone. Londoners were able to build a beautiful new City, having new brick and stone houses, in place of the old shabby wooden buildings they once knew.

(C)   *Fire spreads.* The children were going by school bus to the beautiful seaside town of Newcastle, in County Down, Northern Ireland. (There are at least, two other "Newcastles" in England. Does anyone know where they are?) When the children arrived at Newcastle, they were pleased that their Teachers had arranged for them to go on a short climb on the Slieve Donard mountain for the afternoon. This is the lovely part of Ireland, described in the song; "Where the Mountains of Mourne sweep down to the sea."

The children climbed up the mountain paths, and were amazed to see, what appeared to be roads, high up on the mountain among the Pine forests. The children asked a Forester why there were such straight grass roads in the forest, high up on the mountain. The Forester, smiled at the children. He told them that the grass roads were really "fire-breaks," which enabled the fire-fighters to get up quickly to the source of the outbreak of a fire.

He explained that "On a windy day, fire spreads faster than children can run. We need Fire-breaks." The children happily returned down the mountain, having learnt in a practical manner, why Foresters are so strict about people not lighting fires in a forest. Because Fire spreads so quickly, it is very foolish to play with matches or inflammable materials.

(D)   *Fire warms.* Have you noticed that when people sit together in a room, they usually sit facing the fireplace. Fires may be made from logs, or coal, or peat, or gas, or electricity. If you have a cat or a dog, you will know that animals love to lie beside a fireplace. The only time they forsake the fireplace is on a warm day, when the rays of the Sun come shining in through the window.

Cats and dogs love to lie in the warmth of the sunshine. The Sun is like a large fire burning high up in the skies. During the Winter the ground is very cold, but as Spring time comes round, the fire in the sky begins to warm the ground. Plants begin to peep through the soil and grow again.

Most children know the story of how Peter became afraid of the enemies of Jesus. Did you know that Peter denied that he was one of the disciples of Jesus, while he was warming himself at the fire?

(E)   *Fire may go out.* When we make a bonfire it burns brightly, especially in the darkness. After it burns its brightest and fiercest, the fire comes to a point were it dies down and eventually goes out. Usually, next morning, we may find just a heap of ashes, where once flames burned brightly. Did you know that enthusiasm is very like a fire? We all may begin a task with great enthusiasm. Then we lose interest. Our enthusiasm sometimes is like a fire that is just going out.

Prayer:

> We thank you, Lord, for the warm sunshine.
> We thank you for the warmth of God's love
> for all children everywhere.
> May the fires of enthusiasm burn in us,
> that we may be keen to do what is good and right.
> Bless the needy children of the third world,
> and make us kind and warm-hearted.   Amen.

Hymn:

> Colours of day dawn into the mind. (C&P. 1. 55)

Teachers' Note: (1) Like a fire, children may attract attention. (2) Like the new building programme, after the great fire of London, children may start afresh after a making a mistake. (3) Just as a fire spreads, so childrens' good deeds may spread far and wide. (Just as in the Bible story, the boy who gave his lunch to Jesus, helped to feed the five thousand people.) (4) Just as fire warms, so we may be warm-hearted and friendly. (5) Fire may go out. Our enthusiasm and keenness in a good cause may fade away.

(c) Jacob's Ladder

For effect, the opening story may be told slowly with dramatic skill, leading up to its climax.

There was once a boy, who was climbing up a beautiful mountain, The mountain was very high. It had one large cave at the foot of the mountain, and another four smaller caves higher up the cliff face. The boy entered, and looked around the first cave. He decided to climb to the fifth cave which was high up on the sheer rock face.

He began to climb up the rocks. He soon reached the second and third caves. He continued to climb moving to the right, and then to the left, edging carefully up the cliff-side. He reached the fourth small cave. He clung to the rocks, as he climbed again. He had almost reached the fifth and highest cave of all.

Looking down below, he was terrified that he had reached such a dizzy height. He had been holding on to a small bush growing out of the rocky ground. To his horror the roots of the bush began to pull out of the rocky soil. The boy climber felt himself, … falling … and falling … down … down … down. He called out for help, as loud as he could. He held himself tightly, until he hit the rocks below with a heavy thud.

The boy opened his eyes with trembling fear, to find that he was lying on the bedroom carpet, holding on to a sheet. IT HAD ONLY BEEN A DREAM, and he had just fallen out of bed. He crept back into bed again, and tried to calm himself down. He never forgot that dream! He was glad that he was safe after all. He closed his eyes again, and went fast asleep.

Dreams can seem to be so very real. Dreams are usually caused by past events. Sometimes if we are unwell, we may dream a lot. In the Bible, we are told that God often talked to people by means of a dream.

Esau and Jacob were two brothers. The brothers were grown men. They had a quarrel, and Esau made up his mind to kill Jacob. However, Rebekah, their mother, warned Jacob that Esau was so angry, that he intended to kill him. She advised Jacob to escape while there was time. Jacob travelled away from his home, going towards a place named Haran. It was evening time, and the sun was going down in the Western sky. Jacob was very tired with his long journey, so he took a stone for a pillow, and lay down. He fell fast asleep.

Jacob had a dream that night which changed his life. He dreamed of a ladder which was set up on the earth. This ladder went right up into the sky, and reached up to Heaven. Jacob saw angels walking up and down this ladder. The Lord stood at the top of the ladder, looking down at Jacob.

Then the Lord spoke to Jacob. He said, "I am the Lord God of Abraham, and the God of Isaac. The land where you are now, I will give to you, and to your children, and to your children's children. Your descendants upon the earth, will become many. Your children will spread North, South, East, and West. Every family on earth will be blessed through your family. I will guard you, Jacob, everywhere you go."

Jacob woke up from his sleep. Jacob was afraid, because he realised that God had been in that place. Although there was neither Temple nor Church there, yet Jacob called that place, "Bethel," which means the "House of God." Early in the morning, Jacob took the stone which he had been using for a pillow, and he made it into a pillar (as a memorial stone) unto the Lord. He poured oil on the pillar, as an offering unto the Lord.

Jacob made an important decision at that moment. He said, "If God will guard me on my journey. If he will give me bread to eat, and clothes to wear, and if I return home to my father's house again, then the Lord God shall be my God. I will give to God one tenth of everything I own."

Jewish people, ever since, give to the Lord, what is called a "Tithe." Out of every ten pounds which Jacob earned, he promised to give God one pound. If Jacob had one hundred sheep, he gave ten of them to the Lord. Later, God changed Jacob's name to that of "Israel." (which means a Prince). The story became true. The descendants of Israel spread all over the world.

Prayer:

>Father, we thank you for Jacob's dream.
>We thank you for the meaning,
>that God is near us all, even when we are asleep.
>We thank you that God's house may be found
>is the whole wide world of nature.
>As Jacob gave presents to God,
>may we also offer ourselves to you.   Amen.

Hymn:

>We are climbing Jesus' ladder, ladder. (C&P. 1. 49)

Teachers' Note: Dreams may teach us lessons in life that we should remember. (1) Brothers or sisters may become enemies, if we do not forgive each other. (2) Jacob had no need to be afraid in the dark night, because God was near him, as the dream showed. (3) Jacob made a personal vow and promise to God. We all may make private and personal vows to the Lord.

(a) Part of Something Bigger

Today, you are going to hear three short stories being told. You are to listen carefully, and then you are to say in what way the stories are like each other.

The Blanket

The girls decided to form a "Knitting Club". They heard about the cold nights which people experienced in Africa. When they first heard this information, they were very surprised. They all thought that if it was hot during the day, then it must be hot during the night. This is not so. In many parts of Africa it can be very cold at night. The girls agreed to get together, and to make woollen blankets for a West African Hospital.

The girls collected as many balls of wool that they could find. Their mothers, older sisters, aunts, grannies, and neighbours gave them any wool, which had been lying unused at home. Each girl was given a square piece of cardboard, exactly the same size. The girls were asked to knit woollen squares, exactly the same size as the cardboard square.

They brought the woollen squares to school, and sewed them all together to make a set of large blankets. Then, they sewed a sheet on the underside of each blanket. The finished blankets were very attractive looking and brightly coloured. The blankets were carefully packed into wooden tea-chests, and sent by ship to a hospital in West Africa. The girls were happy because they had all worked together on the one project.

Building St. Paul's Cathedral.

A visitor from the United States of America was staying in the city of London, during the time when St. Paul's Cathedral was being built. The American came to watch the many stonemasons, builders, and steeple-jacks who were working on the site of the new cathedral. He was amazed to see how many men were involved in such a large building.

The American visitor went up to one stone-mason who was carving out a block of stone. He asked him, "What are you doing?" The stone-mason who was feeling a little bored with his work, replied, "I am carving this white Portland stone." The American visitor turned away, from the bored stonemason. He saw another man who was carving out another block of stone. He asked the second builder, who was enjoying his work, and had a happy twinkle in his eye, a similar question. He asked, " Now my good man, what are you doing?" The second stonemason stood up straight, and his chest filled with pride. He answered, "Sir, I am helping Sir Christopher Wren, the famous architect, to build Saint Paul's Cathedral."

The first stone-mason only saw the one piece of stone which he was carving. The second stone-mason took a larger view. In his mind he could see that he was helping a great architect, Sir. Christopher Wren, to build the magnificent St. Paul's Cathedral.

The Piccolo

There was once an instrumentalist who was a member of a famous orchestra. He played the tiny instrument known as the "Piccolo". Sometimes he felt a little downhearted because the Piccolo was such a small instrument. It was just about the size of the tin whistle which he used to play when he was a small boy. Although, he realized that the Piccolo had a higher pitch, and was much sweeter in tone.

When he compared his Piccolo with the other instruments of the orchestra, he thought to himself, "The Piccolo makes such a little sound, that no-one would notice anyway, if I stopped playing. All the other instruments have such grand sounds, and they produce such wonderful music. I have decided that the next time the Orchestra gives a Concert in the Hippodrome, I shall not play my instrument. Nobody will notice or care."

The night of the Grand Concert came round, and the Orchestra assembled in the Hippodrome. The audience was made up of the most famous people in the land. A world-famous Austrian Conductor was to conduct the Orchestra as it played wonderful Classical music. The Stringed instruments were tuned up. The Brass instruments were made ready. The Percussion instruments were arranged properly. The wind instruments were set in order.

Then the famous Conductor came out, walking on the stage beside the first Violinist. They bowed to the people. Everyone in the audience clapped their hands in appreciation. The famous Conductor raised the baton in his hand, smiled at the members of the Orchestra, and at once the music broke forth.

It swelled loud and clear in a melodious sound to a great crescendo. On and on, the Orchestra poured out the most stirring music, that moved many of the listeners to tears. At that point, the instrumentalist stopped playing his Piccolo, and set it down by his side. He was sitting in the back row. No-one could see him.

The Orchestral music still seemed to come in waves of beautiful sound. Suddenly the famous Conductor waved his baton, and compelled the Orchestra to stop playing. He called to the Orchestra, "What has happened to the Piccolo? Where is the Piccolo? No orchestra is complete without a Piccolo. We need that high sweet distinctive sound of the Piccolo? Where is the Piccolo?"

The musician stood to his feet, and bowed to the famous Conductor, holding his Piccolo for all to see. The Conductor bowed back to him, everyone clapped for a long time. The Orchestra again began its glorious music, and the musician blew his piccalo as he had never played before. He, at last, had learned of the value of his instrument. He was never downhearted again, because he now knew, that he was an important part of an Orchestra. The Austrian Conductor had actually noticed that the sound of the Piccolo was missing, even though it was a small instrument.

In the three previous stories, the girls, the stone-masons, and the Piccolo were all part of something bigger than themselves. Children are part of a family; part of a school; part of a religion, and part of God's Church. We all belong to something bigger than ourselves. When we say the prayer, "our Father" it means that we all belong to God's family. That is what makes it worth while.

Prayer:
> Father God, we thank for the joy of working together.
> Lord, we thank you for the feeling of unity.
> Holy Spirit, blend our spirits in harmony,
> like instruments of the orchestra.
> Take from our hearts all envy and spite.
> Teach us to love, and to respect each other.   Amen.

Hymn:
> I belong to a family, the biggest on earth. (C&P. 1. 69)

Teacher's Note: (1) Young people may contribute together to help people overseas. (2) Young people may become helpers and builders of Christ's kingdom. (3) The mark of good Orchestra is harmony, and personal contributions. No-one must ever feel left out, or unimportant among God's people.

(b) The Potter   *Week 10   Making Things*

The Children used to watch an Eastern potter make earthenware pots from clay. The potter knew where to go beside the river to get fine soft clay, which had no grit or rough sand in it. He would take the soft clay home, and add water to it. He again mixed the clay, like a baker kneads dough for making bread. The potter worked the clay with his hands, until the clay became like soft smooth cement. He had a little table, which had a flat round top on it. The table was known as the "potter's wheel," because the potter could make the table top turn quickly in a circle, by moving his feet on a pedal.

As the wheel turned round and round, the potter took a handful of soft clay, and actually threw it on the wheel with a slap, to extract any air that might be in the clay. Still the wheel kept whirring round, and the potter's skillful hands, gently shaped the soft clay into a beautiful wine jar. It was such a beautiful jar, that it was fit for the palace of the King. Then the potter used a piece of string at the bottom of the pot to separate the soft clay jar from the round table. (Just like a grocer used cut cheese with very thin wire.)

The potter carefully put the newly made clay jar into a kiln. The kiln was really an oven with a fire inside it. After clay jars have been in the fire of the kiln for many long hours, or sometimes days, they become baked hard. The children came back to watch the potter take the beautiful wine-jar out of the red hot kiln. He set it on a tray to cool. It took many hours to become cold.

The children saw that he had created a most beautiful wine-jar, with a long slim neck. The potter held it in his hands, and inspected it. He smiled to himself, because was proud of his work. He held it carefully up to the light, and suddenly, the smile left his face. He had seen a tiny crack in the beautiful jar. It was no longer perfect. To the children's amazement, with all his might, he threw the beautiful jar on top of other broken earthenware lying smashed in the corner.

The potter began his task all over again. A second time, he threw the clay on the wheel, carefully shaped the clay, and again put another jar into the hot kiln. Again he waited long hours until the second jar was thoroughly baked hard.

Again, he took it out and placed it to cool. Once more he examined the newly made wine-jar . This time there were no cracks in it. The Potter smiled to himself, and at the children. The wine-pot was perfect, as well as being beautiful. The Potter spoke to the children. He said, "Children, nothing but the very best is good enough for me." This time the watching children understood.

Imagine the children's surprise, when the next time they saw the perfect wine-pot, it was in their local church. The congregation had bought the perfect wine-pot from the potter, and they had given it to the church to store the wine used at Holy Communion. The potter was right. Nothing but the very best was good enough for God's service.

What a good thing that the potter had broken the first wine-pot with the crack in it. If he had sold that wine-jar to the church, the wine would have leaked out, and been wasted. The potter was only satisfied with giving his very best.

The problem about doing your best is that no-one really knows whether you are doing your best, except yourself!

Prayer:

> Lord God, we want to offer our best
> in our school work.
> Forgive us if we are half-hearted.
> Teach us, never to offer our second best,
> when we could do better if we tried.

We thank you for crafts-people such as the potter.
Let us not dispair, should we have to begin again.   Amen.

Hymn:

The wise may bring their learning. (C&P. 1. 64)

Teachers' Note: (1) The potter put his heart and skills into his first work. Crafts-people may produce lovely objects. (2) The potter would not offer a second best wine-jar for sale. He aimed at giving his very best. (3) It does no harm to make a second attempt at anything that we do not get quite right the first time. We ought always to offer our best to God. (A story about a potter is found in Jeremiah Chapter 18 verses 1-6 which is suitable for older children.)

(c) Printing Good Books

Week 10   Making Things

For hundreds of years after Jesus died, there were no printed books. Books had to written out by hand using, a large feather as a quill-pen. The writer was often a monk who lived with other monks in a monastery. Monks had plenty of time to write books, and to translate foreign languages. They dipped the sharp end of the feather into the ink, and they wrote on single pages of parchment.

The books were beautiful because they were illuminated (decorated) with red, blue, and gold drawings. It was a successful way of writing, but it was very slow method. It took a long time to write one book. If many books were needed, then a number of monks had to copy out one book each. The most famous of these hand produced books was written in Ireland, and is known as the," Book of Kells."

During the fifteenth century, there was once a boy who lived in the town of Mainz, which is in Germany. His father was the Master of the money factory, which is called a "Mint". (In Britain nowadays, the Mint is situated in London, and it is the part of the Bank of England which makes all our money.)

This boy was born in the year 1397. He was named Johann Gutenberg. Because his father was the Master of the Mint, the boy Johann was allowed to see the workers making gold and silver coins. First, the metal-workers cut the gold and silver into circular shapes. Next, the craftsmen, used to stamp words, and a picture of the the Kings' head on each coin, just like our money today.

The goldsmiths and silver smiths used a hammer, and a short hard iron punch which had a letter of the alphabet on the end of it. Each time the worker hit the punch with a hammer, it left a letter or a number on the softer gold or silver coins. Johann loved the Mint so much, that he became a craftsman in metal.

Johann wondered if the alphabet could be made of metal letters, and put in long rows, to print words on paper. (Just as children can cut patterns on a potato and then dip the potatoes in ink or paint, and print designs on a page.) Johann Gutenberg invented the first printing press. In 1456 he printed 300 Bibles. Each Bible had 1282 pages. It was a slow process, because he could only print one page at a time. Yet it was hundreds of times faster than writing a book by pen. From that time onward, printing presses were made, and thousands of books were printed around the world.

Nowadays, if your school has a computer and a printer, even children could make a book. If you make a mistake as you type with the key-board, you can easily remove the wrong word, and type in the correct word.

One day at the Village Primary School, the children decided to write two stories to be included in the school's Annual Year-book, which was published on 1st. April, which was all Fools Day. The girls and boys helped each other with ideas. The two stories which follow are supposed to come from the Bible. Can you discover which story is the correct one?

First Story   (*Read very slowly*)

"The first man whom God created was called, "Abraham." When Abraham fell asleep, God made Martha, the first woman. She became Abraham's wife. They both lived in the Garden of Jericho. God said that they could eat the fruit of any tree in the garden, except the orange tree. A Parrot spoke to Martha, and tempted her. Martha offered an orange to Abraham from a tree in the garden. However, Abraham refused it. Martha ate the orange herself. She made clothes from animal skins, for both Abraham, and herself, because they were cold. They both tried to hide from God in the bushes, but God called them out. God sent an archangel with a flaming sword, to put Abraham and Martha out of the beautiful garden. The Parrot flew away."

Second Story   (*Read very slowly*)

"The first man whom God created was called Adam. He lived in the garden of Eden, with Eve his wife. God said that they could eat the fruit of any tree in the garden, except one particular tree. (The fruit of the Tree of the knowledge of good and evil.) A Serpent spoke to Eve, and tempted her to eat the forbidden fruit. Eve offered the forbidden fruit to Adam. They both realised that they were naked. They sewed fig leaves together to make clothes. God put them both out of the Garden of Eden. He sent an angel with a flaming sword to guard the gates of the beautiful garden. Adam and Eve were never allowed to live in the garden again."

Now you may raise your hand to vote for which story is the correct account from the Bible. Hands up for the first story. Hands up for the second story? What we have learned today is that not everything which we have read is true. Not everything we write is correct. We may tell lies with our pen. We may write unkind words about other people. God is pleased with us when we read good books about his beautiful world. The Bible has sixty six books all bound together under one cover.

Prayer:

Heavenly Father, we thank you for books
and the knowledge we gain from them.
We thank you for all Holy books.
May we read them with care.
Bless blind children who read Braille books.
We thank you for the English language,
and all other languages.   Amen.

Hymn:

The ink is black, the page is white. (C&P. 1. 67)

Teachers' Note: (1) The early Scriptures were all hand-written. (2) Johann Gutenberg's printing press was a most wonderful invention. It was a cheaper and quicker method of producing books. Poor people could read ideas for themselves. (3) The Bible is full of very interesting stories.

(a) The Best Day of the Week   *Week 11   About Sunday*

Sally loved nursery rhymes. She knew many of them off by heart. She loved to repeat;

"Solomon Grundy
Born on Monday,
Christened on Tuesday,
Married on Wednesday,
Took ill on Thursday,
Grew worse on Friday,
Died on Saturday,
Buried on Sunday.
And that was the end
Of Solomon Grundy."

Sally knew that Solomon Grundy might have lived to be a very old man, because all these experiences could not have happened on the one week.

She asked herself which day of the week she liked best. Sally decided that the day she liked best, was a Sunday. First of all, Sunday was a holiday from school. There was something different about a Sunday. Usually, she went to the Junior Church, with her friends from the youth club.

In Summer weather, Sally often went with her family in the car to the Lake District. She loved Keswick and Ambleside. Sometimes when in Bowness, the whole family would take a boat trip up Lake Windermere. That really was exciting! On other occasions, they would walk around Lake Buttermere. Even when it was raining, it was good fun. Sally decided within herself that Sunday was a good day for visiting the Lake District, except that there was a lot of traffic on the roads coming home.

If the family was at home on Sunday, Sally knew that they always had a special dinner. Just like most other children, Sally liked good dinners such as, roast beef, or roast chicken, with all the extra vegetables. She loved to have apple pie and custard, with a large spoonful of ice-cream on top. The hot custard always melted the ice-cream, and the white cream flowed round the plate.

Sally had a very old Grandma. She always went to her Grandma's house for her Sunday evening's tea. Grandma had old fashioned cups, and saucers, and plates, and a tea-pot with a woollen tea-cosy around it, to keep the tea warm. Grandmas are usually very good at baking cream cakes, and cakes with icing on the top. Best of all, after tea, Sally's Grandma was very good at telling stories about her own childhood. Grandma had one special old chair, covered in red velvet. She told Sally always to be careful with the old chair because it was the "Queen's Chair".

One Sunday, Sally asked her Grandma to tell her the story about the old chair. Grandma agreed to do so. She said, "My Grandma, your Great grandma, your great grannie, lived during the nineteenth century, when Queen Victoria was on the throne. One Sunday, the Queen came to visit the town. She was to open the new "Victoria Public Park" at the end of the street. She travelled with her coach and horses, and many servants, because there were no motor cars on the roads in those days. However, the Queen arrived an hour too early. Someone had written down the wrong time for the opening ceremony."

Grandma's eyes sparkled, as she told the story. "The Queen looked down the street, and she saw that our front door was open. She came out of her royal coach, and knocked on my front door. My Grandma, was surprised at seeing Queen Victoria standing on her doorstep, on a Sunday afternoon. "Come right in, your Majesty, she said, as she curtsied to the Queen". The Queen sat down on my Grandma's red velvet chair, right beside the fire, while her servants stood outside. "I'm tired waiting in the coach outside the new Public Park. I seem to have come an hour too early." Queen Victoria said. "Please make me a cup of tea."

"My Grandma, quickly made the Queen a cup of tea, using her best china cups and saucers. She put a piece of cherry cake on the plate. The Queen ate it, every crumb, and helped herself to a second piece. Grandma was delighted that the Queen liked her cake. The Queen said that she loved Sunday, because it was different from the week days.

My Grandma agreed that "A Sunday well spent, brings a week of content." The Queen looked at the clock. The hour had passed by very quickly. "I must be off, now, to open your new Public Park," she said. Grandma curtsied again, as the Queen said "Goodbye".

Grandma said to Sally, "Now you can see just why I call that chair the "Queen's chair". I suppose that I am a little old fashioned, but I really do love a Sunday. It is a day of rest, and recreation. "Recreation" means making afresh a new spirit inside you. So whether you rest, or walk, or worship, it makes us feel like new people inside ourselves. God gives us one day in every seven to use as a special day. Jesus rose from the dead, on the first Easter Sunday. The disciples called it, "The Lord's day. That is why we keep Sunday special". Grandma allowed Sally to sit on her special red velvet chair every Sunday evening.

Prayer:

Heavenly Father, we thank you for the Lord's day.
Help us to use our Sunday for worship,
or for rest, or for recreation.
May we make Sunday a day of friendship.
May we all come back to school
renewed in body and mind.
Through Jesus Christ our Lord.   Amen.

Hymn:

All creatures of our God and king. (C&P. 1. 7)

Teachers' Note: (1) Sally really enjoyed her Sundays, whether she was at home, or in the Lake district. (2) Sally's Grandma certainly loved children. (3) Sunday is a helpful day, whether we worship, or rest, or recreate our strength.

(b) People Who Work on Sunday   *Week 11   About Sunday*

Many people have to work on a Sunday. They have to make some other day their special day. The Captain of a ship has to work on a Sunday on his voyage over the sea. The hospital doctors and Nurses are on duty on many Sundays of the year. The Firemen are on duty every Sunday, in case a fire breaks out on that day. Many people in a newspaper firm have to work on a Sunday in order to produce the newspapers for Monday morning.

Jesus was once rebuked by the Pharisees, because he had healed a sick man on the Sabbath day. Jesus defended his good deed, by asking a question of the people, who were finding fault with him. He said, "If a farmer has an ox, (cow or bull), and it falls into a hole on the Sabbath day, is it not right that he should pull the poor beast out of the hole. Surely, then it is right that I should heal this sick man on the sabbath day." The fault finders had nothing to say.

On another occasion, there was a lady whose back had been stooped for eighteen years. She was bent so much by her illness that she walked with her head tilted towards the ground. It was the Sabbath day, and Jesus touched her and healed her. He made her well. Immediately, her back was made straight and she walked in a normal manner. The Pharisees again found fault with Jesus, because he had healed on the Sabbath day. Jesus called them hypocrites, because he said that they all worked, when they led their cattle to the water-hole on a Sabbath day. Healing people was his good work, on a good day.

A modern Sunday parable

Many people have to work on Sundays. Mr. Grainger and Mrs. Noble were "Para-medics." This means that they were specially trained people who knew how to save lives, by giving first aid, even in serious cases. They drove the ambulance and rushed to scenes of accidents to give help to casualties. They gave medical help, even before the casualties were brought to the hospital. Ambulance-people are on duty any day of the week.

One stormy Sunday morning, a tree had been blown down. It had fallen on top of a house. The house was a bungalow type of house. All the rooms were on the one level. When the tree fell, it had crashed through the roof, Mrs. Baker had been lying in bed when the ceilings caved in, and the tree crushed the walls, it was so heavy. The Anderson family across the street, heard the noise, and looked out. They saw what had happened. Walter, the oldest boy, phoned 999, and wisely asked for Ambulance, Fire-brigade, and Police.

People who were going to church that morning, watched as the ambulance arrived very quickly, with the para-medics, Mr. Grainger and Mrs. Noble. They were soon making their way through the rubble and bricks, when the fire-tender arrived, followed by the Police. They found that Mrs. Baker was pinned down in her bed by branches of the tree.

The firemen soon cut the branches away, using an electric saw, and their fire axes. Mr. Grainger and Mrs. Noble gave Mrs. Baker an injection to ease the pain in her legs. They carefully carried her to the ambulance on a stretcher. The Police put a guard outside the old lady's house, to protect her belongings.

The Police car, with its blue light flashing, drove ahead of the ambulance in order to clear the road, so that the ambulance could get the patient to the hospital quickly. The ambulance was flashing its orange light, and sounding its siren. The two Para-medics acted quickly, because they knew that the lady might have had internal injuries.

At the hospital, the Nurses and Doctors were ready to give the lady an X-Ray to discover what bones were broken. They dressed her wounds, and put her into a warm hospital bed. The Ward Sister was warned that she must keep one nurse to watch, the electronic machine, which was placed by the bed, to measure Mrs. Baker's heart-beat rate, and her temperature. The hospital Chaplain called in to see how Mrs. Baker was recovering.

The people at the church noticed that Mrs. Baker's pew was empty that Sunday morning. So, some of them visited the hospital to see if Mrs. Baker needed any help. Mrs. Baker had suffered a terrible shock, and her leg had been broken. However, she soon recovered. Everything that was good had happened, because some people had worked on a Sunday. The better the day, the better the deed.

Prayer:

Loving heavenly Father,
we thank you for every day of the week.
We praise you for the one special day,
when we can rest, and renew ourselves.
May we use Sunday as a special day for worship.
Bless everyone, who is expected to work on Sunday.
Especially, we pray for hospital workers.   Amen.

Hymn:

If I had a hammer, I'd hammer in the morning. (C&P. 1. 71)

Teachers' Note: (1) Jesus showed us that it is good to help people on a Holy day. (2) Someone has to work on a Sunday to keep emergency services going. (3). Sunday is a special day for worship, for rest, and for recreation.

(c) Two Royal Visits (for Palm Sunday)   *Week 11   About Sunday*

The Irvine Queen Mary and her four Mary's

Irvine in Ayrshire, is now known as a "New Town" because most of the houses and roads have been built quite recently. However, Irvine is really one of the oldest towns in Scotland. It was once the port for the City of Glasgow. The children of Irvine love the "Marymass Fair" celebrations, which nowadays is a peoples' celebration, held during the third week of August.

, One girl from a Secondary School is chosen to represent Mary Queen of Scots, for the celebrations. Four other girls are chosen to be the Queen's four royal Ladies in Waiting, who in Scottish history, also all happened to be named "Mary". (Mary Seaton, Mary Beaton, Mary Fleming, and Mary Livingstone). The girls are robed in beautiful dresses. On Marymass Saturday, the girl acting as Queen Mary with her four attendant Mary's, ride through the streets of Irvine in specially decorated coaches.

In front of the Town's House, (Town Hall), a red carpet is laid out on the street for the royal party. They walk up steps to a raised platform. Mary is crowned Marymass Queen for the day. After the Coronation ceremony, a parade of Bands, and children walk through the streets waving to the people. The Provost (Scottish Mayor) with the Town Councillors, are also in the procession. They are accompanied by Queen Mary and her four Mary's, riding in coaches, just as if she were a real Queen.

Hundreds of people line the footpath. They wave as the girls go past in the royal procession. On the moor just outside the town, Horse races, and a fun fair are held. Local boys climb up a greasy high pole for a prize. Everyone enjoys the feasting. The girls have a happy day which they will always remember. What makes it so real, is that the adults and the children all act their parts together, in a procession that looks as if it just came out of the history book.

The first Palm Sunday Procession

The procession at Irvine reminds us of the events on the first Palm Sunday. Jesus sent two of his disciples to the next village. He told them that they would find a young donkey ready, and tied to a post. Jesus told the two men that they were to un-tie the rope, and bring the donkey to him. He said that if anyone saw them, and questioned what they were doing with the donkey, that they were just to say, "The Lord has need of him."

The two disciples went off to the village as they were told to, and sure enough, there they found the donkey tied to a post. Just as they were loosening the rope that held the donkey, the owners came along. They said, "Why are you loosing the donkey?" The disciples answered exactly as they were told by Jesus. They said, "The Lord has need of him." They brought the donkey back to Jesus. It would seem that Jesus had already made a private arrangement beforehand with the owners of the donkey.

As the disciples and Jesus came down the road to Jerusalem from the Mount of Olives, Jesus sat on the donkey's back. The disciples had put their clothes on the donkey, making a soft saddle for Jesus. (Kings going to war to kill people, always rode on war-horses.) However, it was the custom that when a King was coming to a city in peace, that he rode on a donkey. No-one would ever run away in fear from such a King.

As Jesus rode through the streets of Jerusalem that day, the people, with their girls and boys, lined the way. They shouted "Hosanna, in the highest. Blessed is he who comes in the name of the Lord. Hosanna! Hosanna!" (Hosanna did not mean , "Hip hip hurray." Rather, it really meant , "Save us now!")

There was no red carpet to put down on the road on that day. Instead, the people cut down leaves from the Palm Trees, and laid them on the ground, before King Jesus. The twelve disciples were happy, because at last, the people accepted Jesus, not just as a prophet, but also as the King of peace.

Ever since that happy day, the Churches celebrate Palm Sunday, by Christians wearing Palm leaves, or by putting Palm branches in the Church vases instead of flowers. Some Churches actually put green leaves on the floor, up the aisles to the front of the pulpit, and to the Lord's Table. This is a good way of reminding ourselves of the first Palm Sunday. It is rather sad that the only crown that Jesus ever wore on his head was a crown of thorns.

Prayer:

Lord God, our Heavenly Father,
we are glad, that on the first Palm Sunday,
Jesus came riding through Jerusalem,
seated on a Donkey.
We are glad that the people with their children
shouted Hosanna, as a welcome to Jesus.
As we draw near Palm Sunday again,
may we also welcome Jesus into our hearts.   Amen.

Hymn:

Trotting, trotting through Jerusalem. (C&P. 1. 128)

Teachers' Note: (1) The children of Irvine in Scotland re-inacted their past. This makes history come alive. (2) Keeping Palm Sunday is also a re-inacting of New Testament history. (3) Jesus always makes his appeal to everyone as individuals, because crowds sometimes have a strange way of changing their minds later. References; (Matt. 21. 1-11. Mark. 11. 1-11. Luke 19. 29-44. John. 12. 12-19.)

(a) The Traitor

Week 12   Towards Easter

Jesus and his twelve disciples were having a special meal in an upstairs room. In those days they did not sit on chairs. Instead, as the custom was, they gathered around a low table on the floor. They reclined in a circle, leaning on one elbow. Jesus looked very seriously at his twelve disciples. He said, "One of you who is sharing this meal with me, is going to betray me." The disciples were really shocked at his words. Each one asked, "Lord is it I."

By this time, Judas had previously made an agreement with the Chief Priests to betray Jesus, if they would give him thirty pieces of silver. Judas took the thirty pieces of silver, and put them into his pocket. He waited for an opportunity to betray Jesus to the authorities. As the meal continued that evening, Judas arose from the table, and quietly went out the door into the darkness of the night. He went off to tell the Chief Priests where Jesus could be found. The meal ended with Jesus and his friends in the upper room singing a hymn together.

It was dark when Jesus went into the Garden of Gethsemane. He had invited Peter, James and John, to come with him. The other disciples he left behind. Jesus needed to pray for strength, because he knew that he would soon be arrested. He prayed, to his Heavenly Father, that his cup of suffering should pass from him. He meant that if it was God's will, that he should not have to die on a cross.

However, Jesus was never afraid of dying. As he prayed for all of us, large drops of blood poured from his forehead like sweat. "Lord," he asked, "Let this cup pass from me, but if not, let not my will, but your will be done." As Jesus was praying, Peter, James, and John, were also in the Garden, a short distance away. They had fallen fast asleep, when they were supposed to be watching, and praying. Jesus woke them, saying, "Why could you not watch with me for one short hour?"

By this time, Judas arrived in the darkness with the Priests, and a company of men armed with swords and staves, to arrest Jesus. Judas had given the enemies of Jesus a secret sign, since in the dark it would be difficult to recognise Jesus. He told them that the person whom he would greet with a kiss on side of the cheek, (as Eastern people greet each other), this was Jesus, the man to be arrested.

The armed company surrounded Jesus and his three disciples. Judas went up to Jesus, and said, "Hello Master." and kissed Jesus on the side of the cheek, as he had arranged. They quickly arrested Jesus, and took him to the house belonging to Cai-a-phas, who was the high Priest. Peter was terrified of also being arrested, yet he loved Jesus in his heart. Peter followed, lingering a little behind the men who had arrested Jesus, following them to the door of the High Priest's house. Judas the traitor, mingled in the darkness with the enemies of Jesus.

Prayer:

Heavenly Father, as we draw near to Easter Week,
we are thankful that Jesus and his friends,
held the Last Supper together.
We remember how he prayed in the garden,
and that he was willing to die on a cross.

Give us more of his love in our hearts.
for each other.   Amen.

Hymn:

Jesus in the garden, sad and left alone. (C&P. 2. 129)

Teachers' Note: (1) The last meal which Jesus shared with his disciples is known to us all by various titles. (The Last Supper, The Lord's Table, Holy Communion, The Mass, The Eucharist.) (2) Judas was a man with special gifts. Jesus chose him to be the treasurer for the band of disciples. (3) Gardens often remind us of the nearness of God. It was in the Garden of Gethsamane, where Jesus prepared himself to face dying on a cruel cross.

(b) Pilate's Part

Week 12. Towards Easter

Because the Jewish Leaders had no power to kill Jesus, they brought him to Pilate, the Roman Governor of Judea. There was a Court trial. Pilate sat in the seat of judgement. The Jews had accused Jesus of stirring up the people in rebellion, and of telling them not to pay their taxes. They said that Jesus had claimed to be a King.

Pilate the Roman Governor could not find any crime that Jesus had committed. Strangely, his wife had sent him a private message. She had not been able to sleep the night before, because thoughts about what the people were doing to Jesus, had disturbed her so much. She advised her husband not to harm Jesus, because he was an innocent man. Pilate could not find any crimes committed by Jesus. He desperately tried to find a way of setting Jesus free.

It was the custom in those days to allow a prisoner to be released each year, at the the Feast of the Passover. Pilate thought that this would be a good opportunity of not having to condemn Jesus to death. There happened to be a rebellious man in prison, named Barrabas, at that time. He had been a robber. Pilate thought to himself, "the people can make the choice, and I can escape making my personal judgement on Jesus."

The soldiers brought Barrabas from the prison. Pilate ordered Barrabas and Jesus to be brought before the people, who had gathered outside the Court in a crowd. Pilate spoke to them. "Whom do you want me to set free, Barrabas or Jesus?" The crowd shouted, "Set Barrabas free!" Pilate asked them, "What shall I do with Jesus, who is called Christ?" The people shouted back, "Nail him on a cross. Crucify him! We do not want him as our King."

Pilate handed over Jesus to the soldiers, and ordered that Barrabas should be set free. Then he called for a basin of water, and he washed his hands before the people. This washing of his hands meant that he was not responsible for the death of Jesus. It was as if he was washing any responsibility for Jesus off his hands, and putting the blame on the people.

The Roman soldiers took Jesus, and whipped him across the back. They made a mockery of him. They pretended that a seat was a king's throne. The soldiers dressed Jesus in a scarlet robe, and made him sit on the seat. They bowed before Jesus as if he were some royal King.

Kings wear crowns, so the soldiers made a crown of jagged thorns, and pushed it down on to his head. They spat on Jesus. They put a reed from the river-side in his hand, as if it were a royal sceptre. The cruel soldiers pretended to bow before him, and again they mocked him. They called out, "Your Majesty, King of the Jews." Then they took off the scarlet robe, and put his own clothes back on him. The soldiers led Jesus away through the narrow streets of Jerusalem to be crucified.

The beatings which Jesus had received made him so weak, that he could not carry the cross-beam of his cross. One of the soldiers forced a man, Simon from Cyrene, who was watching the procession going past, to carry the heavy cross-beam instead of Jesus. Two other thieves had also been sentenced to die, and they were being escorted by the soldiers, along with Jesus that day. Sad to say, most of the other disciples of Jesus had stayed away in fear. Mary, the mother of Jesus, and John the apostle, closely followed the procession to the hill called "Calvary."

The Roman soldiers nailed Jesus, and each of the other two thieves on wooden crosses. They made holes in the ground, and placed the crosses upright. Mary, the mother of Jesus, and John the apostle, did not want Jesus to die alone, so they bravely stood beside his cross. Mary was heart-broken to see her son, Jesus, dying such a cruel death. From twelve o'clock in the day, until three o'clock in the afternoon, it became dark as night, as if a black cloud had blotted out the sun.

Jesus made seven short statements, while he was hanging on the cross. They were "Father, forgive them for they do not know what they are doing." To one of the thieves, he said, "Today, you will be with me in Paradise." To Mary and John, he said, "Mother behold your son! Son, behold your mother." He said, "I am thirsty." He repeated Psalm, 22. verse 1. "My God, My God, why have you forsaken me" Then with certainty, he prayed, "Father, into your hands I commit my spirit." With his last breath, he shouted out, "It is finished!" Then Jesus died.

Prayer:

Heavenly Father, we admire the bravery of Jesus.
We admire the love which Jesus had for his mother, Mary.
We are glad, that he left her to the care of the Apostle John.
Teach us that like Jesus, we too must forgive our enemies.

Show us the meaning of the cross of Jesus,
and that God loves us all.   Amen.

Hymn:

I danced in the morning. (C&P. 1. 22) or
There is a green hill far away. (J.P. 245)

Teachers' Note: (1) Who was responsible for the cruel cross. Was it, Judas, the Jewish Leaders, Pilate, the crowd, or the Roman soldiers? (All had a part in the death of Jesus.) (2) The cross means so many good things. Bravery, forgiveness, fearlessness, God's presence, salvation, hope, and faith. (3) Christians believe that the cross is only half the story. Good Friday is always followed by Easter Sunday.

(c) Mary Magdalene and Thomas   *Week 12   Towards Easter*

Thomas was afraid, just like most of the other disciples, when Jesus had been arrested. He heard what had happened from the other disciples. He knew that when Jesus had died, that he had been taken down from the cross, and that he had been wrapped in grave clothes, and laid in a tomb in a garden. This tomb was like a cave in the side of a hill. A large heavy round stone was placed at the opening of the tomb, after the body of Jesus had been laid inside it. The Roman authorities had ordered that a seal should be put on the stone, to stop anyone opening the grave, and stealing the body. Thomas had heard all this sad news.

Very early in the morning, Mary Magdalene (Not the same person as Mary the mother of Jesus), came in the darkness to the garden tomb. To Mary's surprise, she found that the stone had been rolled back, and that the grave was empty. She thought that someone had stolen the body, so she ran to tell Peter and John.

When they heard the news, they ran to the tomb. John ran faster than Peter, and he reached the tomb first. He looked into the tomb, but he did not go inside it. They discovered that although the grave clothes were still lying wrapped, but flat on the ground, there was no body. Peter and John went home puzzled, because they did not understand that Jesus should rise from the dead.

Mary Magdalene was alone outside the garden Tomb, and she was crying. She too had looked inside the tomb. She saw two angels dressed in white clothes. One was sitting where the head of Jesus would have been, and the other was sitting at the feet. The angels asked her why she was crying. Mary replied, "They have taken my Lord away, and I do not know where they have laid him."

Mary Magdalene turned away, and moments later another person repeated the question. "Woman, why are you crying?" Mary thought it was the gardener. Then the stranger quietly called her by her name. "Mary" he said. Mary recognised that it was Jesus and not a gardener. She was so relieved that she clung to Jesus. Jesus told her to go and tell the disciples what she had seen. Mary rushed back to the disciples, and told them that she had spoken to Jesus.

That very same Sunday evening, Jesus appeared to the disciples, who had gathered together, because they were afraid of the people. Although the doors were closed, Jesus appeared, as if he were coming through the doors. He said to them, "Peace be unto you!" Sad to say, Thomas was not there that Sunday evening. When the other disciples told him that they had seen Jesus, Thomas just would not believe them.

Thomas said, "Unless I see the print of the nails in his hands, and feel the wound in his side, I will not believe!" The following Sunday, Thomas happened to be with the other disciples, in the room with the door shut. Suddenly, Jesus appeared in the room, again, as if coming through the closed door. Once more, he said, "Peace be unto you!" Jesus spoke to Thomas. "Thomas, put your finger into the print of the nails in my hands. Put your hand into the wound in my side. Thomas, stop your doubting and believe!"

Thomas knew then that Jesus had really risen from the dead. He was so convinced and sure, that he could only say, "My Lord and my God!"

Jesus said to Thomas, "Because you have seen me, you have believed, Thomas. Blessed are those who believe in me, even though they have not seen me." Thomas was a changed man from that hour. Later he became known as St. Thomas. He became a Christian missionary to Persia, and later to India.

Prayer:

>Our heavenly Father,
>we thank you for Easter Sunday morning,
>when Jesus Christ arose from the dead.
>We thank you for the faith of Mary Magdalene.
>We are glad that Thomas also believed.
>Give us all a faith that will make us better people.   Amen.

Hymn:

>All in an Easter garden. (C&P. 2. 130)

Teachers' Note: (1) Mary Magdalene had a simple faith in Jesus. She was the first person to tell the good news about Easter. (2) Thomas was a different kind of person. He preferred to be sure, before he made any statements about Jesus. (3) Jesus revealed himself to the fearful disciples, and they too believed. They became braver and better people after they understood the meaning of Easter.

Summer Term

(a) The Evacuees

Winston and Tammy were brother and sister. Winston was nine years of age, and Tammy was nearly eight years old. During the Second World War years, they attended a little country village school. They were children from the city of London. They lived in the country because enemy aeroplanes had been dropping bombs on London. These children were known as "Evacuees."

Evacuation meant that the children had to be transported away from London, by bus, or by train, to a safe, peaceful place in the country. Sometimes their mothers went with them. Winston and Tammy's Mum worked in a London factory helping the war effort. Dad had been called up to serve in the army. It was very exciting for Winston and Tammy to be moved to the country, with many other evacuee children.

Winston and Tammy each carried a gas mask in a cardboard box. The string on the gas-mask box was slung over the shoulder like a school bag. The reason that the children carried their gas masks everywhere, was in case enemy aircraft might make a gas attack. All the evacuees were going to have to live in other people's houses.

Winston and Tammy were welcomed by a kind farmer and his wife into their large farm house. They were happy because both children had a large bed-room each. Other evacuees were welcomed into the homes of villagers. Some homes were smaller cottages with beautiful gardens. The evacuees stayed in the village for six years, until the war had ended. Winston and Tammy had to be brave to be evacuees, because they had to live apart from their parents

Winston and Tammy had always understood that milk came out of a bottle, but the country children knew that milk came from a cow. The other town evacuees knew about tramcars, railway engines, and ships on the River Thames. The country children did not know much about these things, but they knew a lot about foxes, weasels, rabbits, and field mice. Winston and Tammy soon learnt to help the farmer to herd his cattle at the farm.

Town children knew a lot about aeroplanes, such as "Hurricanes, Spitfires, and Lancasters," but country children knew about the birds, such as kestrels, magpies, and skylarks. Winston and Tammy were able to share much of what they knew with the country children. The country children soon became good friends with Winston and Tammy, and with all the other evacuees at school. The war dragged on for more than five years, as the the children grew up away from the city.

All the children wished that the war would come to an end, and that peace would come again. Winston and Tammy never watched television, because there was no television in those days. Instead, everyone listened to the radio, although, in those days, it was called the "Wireless".

Winston and Tammy knew that the B.B.C. Announcer, read the News on the radio at nine o'clock every evening. There was always a one minute of silence, just before the News. The silence came just before the Big Ben clock struck nine times. People in Britain used that minute of silence on the radio, to pray for their grown up sons and daughters who were far away from home. Winston and Tammy prayed for their Mum in the London factory, and for their Dad overseas. They also prayed that peace would come again.

After six years of war, the evacuees became excited, when they heard over the radio that peace was near. The kind country people, who had been caring for the children, decided that they would have an open air "Party" on the village green. The problem was that food was rationed. That meant that everyone was only allowed, a little piece of butter or margarine every week. Winston and Tammy were allowed only one egg per week. Sugar, cheese, and tea were very scarce.

When the Evacuees heard that peace had been announced on the radio, they were very excited. As a big surprise, the farmers' families, and the villagers, worked together to provide the kind of "Party" that the evacuees would have enjoyed, if they had been back in London.

The party tables on the green, had a terrific spread of goodies. Can you imagine it? *(Teacher says very slowly!)* .... Chicken and turkey sandwiches; cream cakes; angel cakes; currant squares; plum-duff; home made biscuits; icing-cake; pears and jelly; ice-cream and plums; strawberries or raspberries or gooseberries; and pots of home-made damson and apple jam, and blackberry jelly, from last year's harvest. Tea ... Pop ... fizz ... and lemonade, were all freely available for every girl and boy. (The secret was that everyone in the village had either baked or given something.)

Neither Tammy nor Winston, nor any of the other evacuees had ever seen such a spread of food on the school tables. It did not rain that day. The sun shone warmly. Even the cows, horses, pigs, sheep, and the little lambs, looked through the hedges to see the crowds of children enjoying themselves. It was the month of May, so the villagers had errected a May-Pole on the Village Green. The Teachers organized the children, so that every child could have at least one opportunity, to dance around the May-Pole.

The Vicar, the Methodist Minister, the Catholic Priest, and the Teachers joined hands to say the Grace, before the party began. They read the Selkirk Grace written by Robert Burns, the Scottish Poet.

"Some have meat, and canna eat,
And some wad eat, that want it:
But we ha'e meat, and we can eat;
And sa'e the Lord be thankit.

Tammy and Winston really enjoyed themselves, because *'Peace'* had come to our country! The evacuees afterward remembered that day in 1945, when the church bells rang in thanksgiving to God. It was the happiest day in their lives.

Prayer:

Heavenly Father, thank you for peace.
Bless the people in any part of the world,
who may be facing the sadness of war.
Especially be near the mothers and children.
Teach us that Jesus was the Prince of Peace.
Let us have peace in our world, in our homes,
and most of all, give us peace in our hearts.   Amen.

Hymn:

I'm gonna lay down my sword and shield. (C&P. 2. 142)

Teachers' Note: (1) War always brings sadness, and separation of families. Peace brings rejoicing. (2) God wants all people all over the world to be good friends. (3) The way to bring peace into the world, is to ask God to give us his peace in our hearts.

(b) Terry's medal

Week 1   Peace after War

Terry was a Scout and he loved to wear his Scout Uniform. He was also an evacuee. Terry used to go down to the army camp every Friday, to remind the clerk in the Commander's office, to send an army lorry to the Scout Hall, on the following Saturday afternoon. The Scouts climbed into the army lorry, and they travelled to a nearby seaside town.

The Scouts, usually in groups of four, went around the houses of the town, collecting waste paper in sacks. They left the sacks full of paper at the end of the street, for the army lorry to collect. The army only sent one driver along with the lorry, so the Scouts had the double job of going from door to door collecting the waste paper, and also of loading the sacks on the Lorry.

Terry and his friends did not mind doing this hard work, because they knew that they were helping the War effort. (In those days, everyone had to help the war effort in some way). People were glad to get rid of their old newspapers, and the shops did not want their old cardboard boxes.

Terry and his friends knew that the waste paper would go to a factory, and be turned into paper pulp. This paper pulp would be made into cardboard containers to be used by the army, navy, or air force. Sometimes, as they went around the big houses, they were give a treat, such as a jam tart, or a glass of milk, by some kind lady. They always remembered to say "Thank You."

One Saturday afternoon, Terry joined the other Scouts. They climbed into the army lorry, and travelled to the nearby seaside town. They walked the streets, ringing doorbells, and saying to the householders, "Good day Madam, have you any waste paper to help the War effort?" They must have said those words hundreds of times. There were no plastic bags in those days, so they had to use jute sacks.

Terry, dressed in his Scout uniform, went to one large house. The householder, who was an old lady, told him that she had placed a lot of waste paper at the back of the house. Terry put the waste paper into his sack, and thanked the lady. When she asked him his name, he answered that his name was, "Terry". She smiled and said, "My husband was also called Terry." The boy said, "Thank you for the waste paper," and he went off, down the garden path.

He was just putting the sack down at the end of the street, when he noticed an old cardboard chocolate-box in the sack. He opened the chocolate box, and there lying inside were two medals with ribbons on them. Terry took the box and the two medals back to the old lady in the house. She was surprised to see the Scout back on her doorstep.

When Terry gave her the box with the two medals inside it, she thanked him for his honesty. Then a little tear came into her eyes. She said to Terry, "These medals belonged to my dear husband, who was killed in the First World War. I was clearing out old newspapers helped by my house-maid, and she must have accidently thrown out the box with the medals inside it. The maid probably thought that it was only an old empty box."

The old lady continued to speak, "I would have been very sad , if I had lost my husband's medals. He never came home from the First World War. He was killed somewhere in France." She told Terry that the radio announcer had mentioned that the Second World War in Europe was nearing its end. The lady said to Terry he should listen to the radio news programme. She said, "The day the war ends, Terry, you are to come back to see me here. On that day I will give you a present."

Off Terry carried his sack of paper, to his other three Scout friends in the group. They loaded the sacks into the army lorry. The lorry carried the Scouts back home again. The boys sat on top of the sacks. Terry never told anyone about the old lady and his adventure.

Some weeks later, (the 8th. May 1945), Terry heard the Radio Announcer reading the News. He said that the war in Europe had ended. There had been great celebrations, and rejoicing in the streets of all the big cities.

Terry went round to the old lady's house that afternoon. She smiled at Terry, and said, "Terry, I have been expecting you to come today." She brought the old chocolate box out of a cupboard drawer, and opened it. She took out one of the silver medals, and said to Terry, "I am giving you one of my dear husband's medals from the First World War."

I want you to have it for yourself. I think that you deserve it! I want you to keep it as you would keep a treasure. Remember, that one young soldier, with the same Christian name as yourself, earned it. His name, and his rank, and army number are engraved around the edge of the medal."

Terry thanked her, and he took the precious medal home. Terry carefully kept the medal all his life. He often thought about the brave young soldier, named "Terry" who earned the medal in the First World War. He was glad that the Second World war in Europe had finished, and that peace had really come at last.

Prayer:

Thank you Lord for peace instead of war.
We pray for people who know the trouble
and sadness caused by war in their land.
We pray for an end to all wars, everywhere.
Help us to value peace, and to love each other,
Through Jesus Christ our Lord.   Amen.

Hymn:

I've got peace like a river. (C&P. 2. 143)

Teachers' Note: (1) Terry was a Scout, who with other Scouts, (and Guides) did their part to help our country in war-time, by collecting waste paper. (2) Some old people remember the First World War, as well as the Second World War. Medals are a good reminder of someone we loved, who was in the army, navy, or airforce. We should be thankful to God for our peaceful land today. (3) Christians look upon Jesus Christ as the "Prince of Peace."

(c) The Miller family and the enemy Pilot   *Week 1   Peace after War*

Mrs. Miller lived during the Second World War. Her husband had been "called up" into the air-force, and was serving somewhere in Europe. Mrs. Miller wrote to her husband, Raymond, once every week throughout the war. She kept him in touch with what was happening in her small town.

She had three children; two girls and one boy. The girls were called Cherry, (Cheryl), and Winnie, (Winifred). The boy was called Bernie, (Bernard). The children grew up during the war. When Dad was away from home, the children helped their Mum in many ways. Most of the women had to work in a war factory.

Mrs. Miller was also a member of a local Church.

During these times, the children loved belonging to the Church, because they were so many interesting things happening. The Church people ran a Canteen. The children helped their Mum to serve the teas, and sandwiches to the soldiers and airmen who called. As a part of her work, Mrs. Miller used to visit the older ladies, who knitted socks and gloves, or mitts for the troops. The children used to pack hundreds of pairs of socks knitted by grannies around the town, and send them in boxes to the army camp up the road.

These were terrible times. One dark evening, when the enemy planes had been bombing London, one plane had been shot down. The aircrew had jumped out before the plane hit the ground. They descended by parachute in the darkness of the night. These enemy airmen tried hide somewhere, to avoid being captured, and interned in a British prisoner of war camp.

Next morning, the children took a walk through the fields to see the wreckage of the, enemy plane, which they heard had been shot down during the night. However, the plane had been burned up during the darkness. There was not much wreckage to see. As they walked back home, they noticed that the door of the cow shed was slightly open. Cherry and Winnie looked inside the cow shed, and to their surprise, they saw an enemy airman lying on the straw fast asleep.

The two girls warned Bernie to keep quiet. They dashed home and told their Mum. "What shall we do?" they asked. Mrs Miller said, "Well in the Bible, the apostle Paul said, 'If your enemy is hungry, then you are to give him bread, and if he is thirsty, you are to give him a drink." (Romans Chapter 12 verse 20). Mrs. Miller and the children made a pot of tea, and four big sandwiches for the enemy airman. Next, she 'phoned 999, and told the Police station that the enemy airman was hiding in the cow shed.

When Mrs. Miller and the three children, opened the door, and looked into the shed, the enemy airman was lying injured. He had broken his leg, so he could not run away. Mrs. Miller spoke a little German. She told the airman to eat the sandwiches and to drink the hot tea, because the Police and Home Guard would soon be here to arrest him. The airman was amazed at the kindness shown by the Miller Family. He showed them a photograph of his own wife and family.

Just then, the Home Guard arrived with their rifles at the ready. They arrested the enemy airman, and took him away to a small hospital in the prisoner of war camp. The Captain of the Home Guard asked Mrs. Miller, "Why did you help that enemy Pilot?" Mrs. Miller said, "I am a Christian. The apostle Paul was quoting the teaching of Jesus, when he told us, to give our enemy bread if he was hungry, and to give him a drink if he was thirsty." The Home Guard Captain had also attended Sunday school, so he remembered these words.

Later, the B.B.C. News announcer read the good news to all his listeners. "The War in Europe has ended." Mrs. Miller, Cherry, Bernie and Winnie, were happy that all the families would soon see their soldier fathers and sons again. They were pleased because the enemy Pilot would later go home to his wife and family. The Church bells kept ringing for a long time that day. It was the people's way of thanking God, that peace had come to Britain again. The Miller family were happy that they had shown how Christians should behave, even to an enemy.

Prayer:

Father God, we pray that peace will remain.
May we be guided by the words of Jesus.
Help each of us to forgive our enemies.
Make us all useful people.
Show us that in serving others,
We are serving our good Lord.   Amen.

Hymn:

Make me a channel of your peace. (C&P. 2. 147)

Teacher's Note: (1) The Miller family had a strong link with the Church. Yet they found time to help other people. (2) They did not complain because of the long separation from their Dad who was in the army. (3) They really followed the teaching of Jesus, and the apostle Paul, when they fed the enemy Pilot. (4) They thanked God for sending peace.

(a) David Livingstone   *Week 2   Explorers*

Wee Davy Livingstone was a bright little fellow. He had been born in the year 1813 in a tenement house in the little Scottish town of Blantyre. Tenements are high blocks of flats. A whole family lived either in one room, or in two rooms. If a family had two rooms, the rooms were known as a "butt and ben." This meant an outer and an inner room. Davy Livingstone's parents were very poor. At the age of ten, he had to go to work in a cotton mill.

Davy wanted to be a Doctor, and also a missionary. (A missionary is someone who is sent to do a special task overseas by the Church at home). When he received his first week's wages, Davy bought himself a Latin Grammar Book. He used to prop his school book against the cotton loom at the mill. If he had a moment to spare, he would try to learn more Latin words.

When Davy became older, he was able to attend Glasgow University to study medicine. In the year 1840, he graduated from the University, and became a Doctor. He knew that if he were to become a missionary, he would need to get a missionary society to send him. He joined the London Missionary Society, two years before he had completed his training as a Doctor.

Dr. Livingstone went as a missionary to what is now known as South Africa, in 1841. He began to study the languages of the native people. He became an explorer, as well as a missionary. He travelled around, always discovering new places, and drawing new maps of unknown parts of the country.

On one of these journeys through the African bush, he was with his line of native porters, who carried his baggage, behind him. A fierce lion sprang out of the bush and attacked. The lion caught David by the arm and the shoulder in its sharp teeth. Only by the prompt help of his native carriers did he managed to escape alive. The lion was killed.

His left arm was broken, and became very painful. It took a long time to heal. Later, in 1844, David married a lady called Mary Moffat, who was a missionary's daughter. They raised a family. David wanted to continue as an explorer, so his wife and children went home to live in Scotland.

David Livingstone made three famous journeys across Africa. He often was sick with fevers. He discovered the famous water-falls, and named them "The Victoria Falls" after Queen Victoria. David was working for the British government, and still drawing maps of the African countryside. The reason for this, was that he wanted to discover suitable healthy places, where people from Europe could come and live. He also wanted to stop the Arab Traders capturing the natives, putting them in chains, and selling them as slaves. Livingstone did not like slavery.

For a long time, no-one in England, or America, knew what had happened to Livingstone. Many thought that he must be have been killed by the slave traders, or lost in some far off jungle. Since there were no radios or televisions in those days, it was the newspapers which were interested in the whereabouts of Livingstone.

An American newspaper reporter, named H. M. Stanley, was sent out to search for Livingstone, to find out whether he was still alive. Stanley searched through many African villages. During November 1871 he was on the East side of the Lake Tanganyika, when he was told about a white man being in the next village.

It was here that Stanley and Livingstone met. As they shook hands, Stanley used words that many people now know off by heart. Stanley said, "Dr. Livingstone, I presume."

The two explorers were very pleased to meet each other, especially as Stanley had brought with him, native porters who were carrying much needed medicines and medical supplies. Soon Stanley went back to his newspaper in America to report that Dr. Livingstone was alive after all.

Livingstone continued his work. He became very ill. On the first day of May, 1873, David Livingstone in the native grass house, knelt as usual to say his prayers by his bedside. Later, when his African friends looked into to his room, they found that David had died upon his knees. The Africans carefully wrapped his body in cloths, and faithfully carried it back 1,500 miles to a port on the coast. David's body was taken by ship to England. It was buried in Westminster Abbey. You may want to look at his memorial, next time you visit London.

Prayer:

> Heavenly Father we thank you
> for the life of David Livingstone.
> We thank you for the vast continent of Africa.
> We pray for the African children and their parents,
> that they may know that God is their Father.
> Help them to enjoy their beautiful country
> and to turn it into a place of happiness for all.   Amen.

Hymn:

> Go tell it on the mountain. (C&P. 1. 24).

Teachers' Note: (1) David Livingstone was very poor, but as a boy, he wanted to learn, and become a Doctor. He succeeded. (2) David wanted to make a good use of his medical knowledge, and to destroy the evil slave trade. (3) David in spite of him becoming very famous, always felt that as a Christian, he needed to pray for guidance in the everyday things of life.

(b) Discovering Holland   *Week 2   Explorers*

It was the week after Easter, The Davidson children were going with their Mum and Dad by car to the Netherlands. Their car was pulling a caravan. The Davidson children, Christopher, Tina, Kelly, and little Patrick, all were excited at the thought of going to Holland. Dad said to them, "If you imagine that you are explorers, then you can write down in your note-books any new sights that you discover. The children thought that this was an excellent idea. So they all bought note-books.

They travelled, towing the caravan to the harbour at Harwich. Christopher, especially was excited, as the large passenger ferry boat, opened it doors, to allow cars, lorries, and cars towing caravans, to drive up the ramp. The vehicles were stored in a deck, at the bottom of the boat. The ship sailed away for the Hook of

Holland. The sea was very calm. The Davidsons were able to watch many other ships as they travelled across the North Sea. Christopher, being the oldest, wrote down in his note-book, *"We passed sailing boats, fishing boats, and oil tankers."* The other children soon found the duty-free shop on board the ferry. They enjoyed spending a little money.

After about six hours, the ferry arrived at the docks in the Hook of Holland. The large iron doors opened again, and the car and caravan moved down the ramp. The other children, wrote down, *"Holland, which is only part of the Netherlands, seems to be very flat."* Driving along the roads, Dad lost his way to the Caravan site. He had not brought a very good map. To their surprise, people in other cars stopped, to help them. The Dutch people, told the family the correct roads to take. Christopher wrote, *"What a surprise! Many young people in Holland speak English, and they watch our television programmes in English! Yet we do not know one word of Dutch."* Soon they reached the caravan site. They helped to park the caravan. Soon everyone was in bed.

Next morning, they arose early. The children found the water tap. They filled a round container with water, and rolled it back to the caravan. After breakfast, Dad said to Mum that it was such a lovely day, they should go by car to Keuk-en-hof to see the famous Spring-Flower Garden. On the way to Keuk-en- hof, the four children saw fields of beautiful tulips of every colour. The tulips were not grown mixed in the fields, but grown together in large areas. It looked as if they were admiring a huge patchwork quilt, of yellow, red, pink, purple, white. There were fields of blue, pink, and white hyacinth. The children wrote in their books, *"The bulb-growing district is beautiful in Spring-time"*

When they arrived at the Keuk-en-hof Spring-Flower Garden, Christopher, Tina, Kelley, and Patrick were amazed at the thousands of flowers growing . There were many different varieties of Tulips, Hyacinth, Crocuses, Daffodils, and Narcissi. There were so many colours, and varieties that they just had to write in their books, *"We never knew so many different flowers existed. It is better than the pictures we have on our class-room wall."* The family left by car again, and travelled to Amsterdam. There seemed to be as many canals, as there were streets. They travelled on the water-bus up and down the canals, looking at the Dutch streets and houses.

Next day they went to see how the Dutch engineers enclosed the sea, and then pumped the water out, to make dry land. The children wrote in their books, that *"The Engineers had managed to please both the Dutch fishermen, who needed the waters for fishing, and the Government who who needed more land to enclose."*

On Sunday they went to the Dutch Kirk (Church). The Minister read the words of Jesus in Dutch, from the Sermon on the Mount. Christopher wrote the words down in English. *"Consider the lilies of the field, how they grow. They do not toil nor spin. Yet King Solomon in all his glory, was not clothed like one of these. If God cares for the flowers, which are here today, and gone tomorrow, will he not most surely care for you. You people of little faith."* (Matthew 6. verses 28-29).

The family agreed afterwards that the words of Jesus about flowers specially suited Holland. The Davidsons had ordered a large packet of Tulip bulbs to be delivered to their home later in the year.

All holidays must come to an end. The Davidson family car towed their caravan back to the harbour at the Hook of Holland. In six hours, they had crossed the North sea, and were back in England. They could not write down everything, which they had discovered on their trip to Holland. They knew that memory was sometimes better than any note-book.

Prayer:

    We thank you Heavenly father,
    for the courage of the Dutch people.
    Bless their land which was rescued from the sea.
    Bless all the Dutch Churches and schools.
    We thank you for the beauty of flowers. Amen.

Hymn:

    All creatures of our God and King. (C&P. 1. 7)

Teacher's Note: (1) We are all explorers in this world, because we are always finding new knowledge. (2). Flowers are magnificent in their beauty, They remind us of the goodness of God. Jesus taught us that God cares for us, as he does for flowers. (3) Dutch people are very friendly. They are also very inventive, in their draining of the land, from sea water.

(c) The Twelve Spies

Week 2   Explorers

The Hebrew people had escaped from the land of Egypt. The crowds of people had moved on a journey through the wilderness (desert). God told Moses that he was to send out spies to look over the land of Canaan, which was the land that God had already promised to the Hebrew people, as their own land. Moses chose twelve men, one from each of the twelve Hebrew tribes.

He told the spies to look over the land of Canaan, and to report back to him, whether the native people were strong or weak, and whether the country was good or bad for farming. The spies were to look at the countryside and the cities.

Moses wanted to know everything he could about the people, whether they lived in tents, or in houses behind city walls.

The twelve spies secretly travelled through Canaan, and for forty days, they observed as many things as they could. They returned with their information, and carrying a branch from a vine tree, with large clusters of grapes hanging from it. They also brought some pomegranates and figs. The spies told Moses, that the country was a beautiful place. They described it as a "land flowing with milk and honey." By this description, they meant that it was a fruitful place.

Ten of the spies mentioned that although the country was fruitful, that the people who lived in Canaan were a very tall race of people, and good fighting soldiers. The ten spies said that when they compared themselves to the Canaanites, that they felt themselves to be as small as grass-hoppers. Caleb and Joshua were two of the spies who did not agree with the other ten spies. Caleb reported, "Let us go up at once with our army, we are strong enough to overcome the Canaanites, and to take possession of the land." Joshua said to the people, "Do not rebel against the Lord, and do not be afraid. The Lord is on our side."

The Hebrew people did not believe Caleb and Joshua. They began to throw stones at them. Moses prayed to God, and asked the Lord to forgive the Hebrew leaders who would not enter Canaan because of fear. The Lord sent a plague. Perhaps, some strange illness came upon the ten spies, and they later died. Strange to say, the two spies, Caleb and Joshua, who gave the good report, continued to enjoy health and strength.

The Hebrew people were not allowed by God, to enter the beautiful land of Canaan at that time. They continued to wander in the desert, for forty years. They continued to complain about having to wander in the desert, often hungry and thirsty. After Moses had died, Joshua and Caleb being much older men, by this time, led the Hebrew people into the Promised land. The Hebrews might have entered Canaan forty years earlier, if only they had believed that God was with them as their helper.

People often need a second chance to be happy. Can you think of anyone whom you know, who did not make a success of their first opportunities in life, but did much better when they were given a second chance? God often gives people another chance to make good in life.

Prayer:

    Lord, God, we thank you for the history,
    of the Hebrew people, as told in the Holy Bible.
    We thank you for people of great faith,
    such as Caleb and Joshua.
    Lord, you gave the Hebrew people
    a second chance, to repent and change.

Help us as young people.
Thanks be to God.   Amen.

Hymn:

What about being old Moses. (C&P. 2. 81)

Teachers' Note: (1) Ten spies brought back a bad report, and only two spies brought back a good report. (2) The difference between the spies was that ten lacked faith, and were afraid. Only two of them believed in God's help, and had courage. (3) It is good to take up a second chance, when we fail in the first chance. Yet second chances in life, do not always come. Ref; Numbers Ch. 14.

(a) Freddie Fly and the spider's web   *Week 3   Leading Others*

Everyone has played the game known as "Follow the Leader." Did you ever play "Simon says"? Did you know that children often follow each other? Next time someone in class yawns, just you watch the other children, and you will discover that others will also begin to yawn.

Freddie the fly had been born in a crack in the wall behind the gas cooker in the kitchen. Mrs. McClean, the cook, believed that cleanliness came next to godliness. Generally speaking, her kitchen was a very clean kitchen, but she forgot to clean occasionally behind the cooker. So it happened that Freddie the house-fly was born. Six days afterwards, it became very warm, and Freddie's little sister fly was also born in the same dirty crack in the wall behind the cooker. Now, there were two little flies buzzing about the kitchen. The youngest fly was named Amanda. Mother-fly warned Freddie to take care of his little sister fly, and always to beware of their greatest enemy, Mr. Spider.

The mother-fly went out through the window, and she was never seen again. Freddie and Amanda became hungry, and flew over the table to the cream cakes which Mrs. McClean had baked. The two flies had a good meal, eating the cream on the top of the cake. The two little flies walked all over the cake, even though they had very dirty feet. None of the children who ate the cake afterwards, ever realised that the two flies had soiled the cake. Indeed, two days afterwards, the children had tummy-aches, but they did not realise that the flies had caused their illness.

The two flies sometimes landed on the butter, or cooked meat, or other food, which cook had forgotten to put back into the refrigerator in the kitchen. All the time, in a cupboard, Mr. Spider was waiting until he heard a fly buzz. The two flies managed to keep out of his way, and eventually flew out of an open window into the garden. Mr. Spider followed them, out the window, and landed among the Lupins at the edge of the garden path. There he made a very large web, between the stems of the lupins. A few silly ants and greenfly soon were stuck in the web, and Mr. Spider ate them up for his breakfast.

The next day, the morning dew had fallen like rain upon Mr. Spider's web. The web really looked beautiful. The wet dew sparkled like jewels on the web, as the sun shone upon it. The two flies flew down to have a look at it.

Freddie buzzed a lot, and stretched his wings. He flew down as close as he dare. Amanda always followed Freddie. She too buzzed a lot, stretched her wings, and flew around the web which was sparkling in the sunshine. "What a lovely design on that web", she thought to herself, "The threads go round and round in a kind of a circle."

Then Amanda forgot all about Mr. Spider. She landed on the web. Immediately, She found that her wings, feet and body stuck to the web, and that the more she wriggled and buzzed, the more she became entangled in the web. Freddie watched in horror, as Mr. Spider ran out from the centre of the web. He caught Amanda, and carried her off for his dinner. Soon he had eaten up the little sister fly.

Freddie flew away. He knew that he was to blame. He had led Amanda down to the spider's web. If he had kept away, his younger sister would still have been alive. That was the end of Amanda. Mrs. McClean never saw Freddie in the kitchen again. One day she thoroughly Spring-cleaned behind the gas cooker, and no more flies were ever born in her kitchen.

Can you think of a good example to set your class-mates?

Prayer:

> Lord teach us to be good examples to others.
> We remember that Jesus was our perfect example.
> May we never forget that others are watching us.
> May we never lead younger children into danger.
> Father, grant us all your protection.   Amen.

Hymn:

> All the animals that I have ever seen. (C&P. 2. 80)

Teachers' Note: (1). We should never allow house flies to infect the food we eat. (2) Freddie, the fly, led Amanda into danger. We are responsible not only for our own actions, but also for the example we set for others. (3) Some practices hold us like a spider's web hold's a fly. It is difficult to escape from them. (Swearing, lying, boasting, and bullying can become sticky habits.)

(b) The Grand Old Duke of York

A group of infant children may be marched up and down the hall, while the school Assembly sing the verse.

The Grand old Duke of York,
He had ten thousand men.
He led them up to the top of the hill,
And he led them down again.
And when they were up, they were up,
And when they were down, they were down.
And when they were only half-way up,
They were neither up nor down.

What does this verse mean? Maybe the Grand old Duke of York was leading a very long column of soldiers, and perhaps, the hill was a very small hill. Therefore, when the long queue of his soldiers reached the top of the hill, they would have to turn back, and march down the hill again.

When there were soldiers at the top of the hill, there would also be soldiers at the bottom of the hill, just beginning the climb. Of course, if there were soldiers at the top of the hill, and also at the bottom, then there must have been a lot of soldiers in between, going up, or going down the hill.

So there were some soldiers at the top, some at the bottom, and some in the middle. Perhaps, to someone who was watching, it all looked to be a little bit of a muddle, but the grand old Duke of York knew what he was doing, and as long as the soldiers obeyed his orders, they would all end up, lined up in straight ranks, at the bottom of the hill. Just like children lining up in a school yard.

Now for a story about a group following each other. Robin was eleven years old, and he was leading the Cub scout pack a short cut, through the shopping arcade. Instead of going up the stairs, Robin led the long crocodile of cubs, up the moving escalator. The younger boys were a little nervous on the moving staircase. As they were going up, Ralph was wearing white trainers on his feet. He had often been told to tie his shoe-laces, because sometime he might stand on them, and then he might trip over, and fall. However, Ralph never bothered listening to what he had been told.

As the Cubs made their way up the escalator, Ralph's shoe-laces became caught in between the escalator steps. He knew he could not get off at the top, so he screamed, "I'm caught by my laces in the metal steps." Robin being the eldest boy, at the top of the escalator, jumped off quickly. He knew that there was an emergency button at the top and bottom of the escalator. He found it, and pressed the button with his thumb. Immediately the escalator stopped. Robin pulled out his Scout knife, and opened the blade. He quickly cut Ralph's shoe lace in two, because Ralph's shoe had been caught, and it had nearly been pulled off his foot. Robin set Ralph's foot free. Ralph really had been frightened. "Thank you Robin for being a quick thinker," he said. "I did not know just what to do!" Robin, smiled. The line of Cubs were standing on every step of the escalator. Robin thought, this is just like the Grand old Duke of York and his ten thousand soldiers. Some of us are at the top, some are at the bottom, and some of us are somewhere in between. The boys going home that evening made up their minds that they would always tie their shoes laces in future.

Did you know that hills are very important in the Bible. They were called "High Places". The Old Testament Prophets would build a little place of worship, usually beside a great stone on the top of a hill. There they could say their prayers to God.

The Jewish Temple at Jerusalem was built on Mount Moriah, where Abraham and his son, Isaac long ago made an altar to worship the Lord.

The most famous hill in the Bible is the hill called "Calvary." This was the hill that the Roman soldiers made Jesus climb, before he was crucified between two thieves. (There are many other hills in the Bible, such as Mount Sinai, sometime called Mount Horeb, where Moses received the ten commandments. Then there was Mount Carmel, where Elijah saw a flash of fire come down from the sky. There is the Mount of Transfiguration, where Jesus clothes became shining white. There is the Mount of Olives, where Jesus was last seen, as he ascended into the clouds.

Prayer:

> Lord, we thank you for the purple hills
> of our own beautiful country.
> We thank you for giving us the strength,
> to climb the green hills and dales.
> We thank you for the lovely views.
> Most of we remember the hill called "Calvary."   Amen.

Hymn:

> We are climbing Jesus' ladder. (C&P. 1. 49).

Teachers' Note: (1) The Grand old Duke of York probably was a good Leader. We all need a good leader sometimes. (2) Robin was also a very good Cub group leader. He had "presence of mind," and he did not panic. (3) Climbing hills is a good, healthy and natural outdoor occupation. The age of the hills have a way of reminding us about the eternal God. "I will lift my eyes unto the hills, from where my help comes. My help comes from the Lord." (Psalm 121).

(c) Abraham's Test

Here is a story that teaches us two things. First, that God puts great value on our lives. Secondly, that no one need ever be killed for the sake of religion.

God called Abraham to leave the land of Ur. God made a promise to Abraham that his descendants, would one day become so many, that he would be known as the "Father of Nations." God told Abraham that his descendents would be as many, as there were stars in the sky at night. By this he meant, that Jewish people would be found all over the world. To Abraham, this all sounded rather strange, because he was very old, and his wife, Sarah, did not even have a child at that time.

It was a surprise, when a little baby boy was born. They called the baby, "Isaac". It seemed like a miracle. Old people do not have children in old age. However, Abraham's family was a special family, under the care of God. Abraham and Sarah loved their little son, and through the years, they watched Isaac grow up into a healthy, happy boy.

The Lord decided to test Abraham, to see whether he loved God, first, before anyone else. God said to Abraham, "I want you to take Isaac, your only son, whom you love. I want you to lead him up Mount Moriah. When you get to the top of the hill with Isaac, I want you to tie Isaac with cords, and put him on an altar of stones. Then I want you to kill Isaac, just as you would kill a lamb, and offer him as a sacrifice unto me." (God was only using words to test whether Abraham would be obedient, or not. God had no intention of harming the boy, Isaac).

Abraham was very sorry to hear God making what seemed to be such a a cruel request. How could a good God ask so much from an old father? Yet Abraham had a very strong faith in God. He absolutely trusted God. Abraham decided to obey God, whatever the cost. Although, to do such a thing, seemed to be very cruel indeed.

Early next morning, Abraham set out for Mount Moriah. He brought Isaac, his beloved son along with him. Abraham did not mention to Isaac what he intended to do. Isaac carried wood for the fire, and Abraham carried his hunting knife with him. Isaac was puzzled that they were not bringing an animal. He said "Father, I see the wood, for the fire, but where is the lamb for the sacrifice?"

Abraham replied, with tears in his eyes, "God will provide a lamb." When they reached the top of Mount Moriah, Abraham built an altar of stones. He put wood to make a fire on the altar. Abraham tied Isaac's hands with cords, and laid Isaac on top of the altar. The old father, took out his hunting knife, and raised it high above Isaac's heart, to kill him.

Suddenly, Abraham heard the voice of God calling him. "Abraham. Stop! Do not harm the boy you love so much. I know now just how much you trust me. I am sure that you will always obey me. I know that you will always do what I ask of you. Look behind you! There is a ram caught by its horns in the bushes. Sacrifice that instead of Isaac."

Abraham, used his knife to cut the cords from off Isaac's wrists. He set Isaac free. Then he took the ram which had been caught by its horns in the bushes. He laid it upon the altar, and killed the ram, and roasted it upon the fire. (They usually ate part of a sacrifice as a meal, after they had offered it to God.)

Abraham and his son, Isaac, went down the hill again, and both were very happy. If Isaac had been killed, then Abraham would have not had any son, to carry on the family name. There would have been no Hebrew or Jewish people in the world, because they are descendants of Isaac.

Abraham was so relieved, because he loved his son with all his heart. Sarah, his mother, was glad that her boy had returned home again. God also was very pleased, because he now knew that Abraham was a man, whom would always obey him.

Prayer:

> Heavenly Father, we admire Abraham
> who loved God more than his own son.
> We are glad that Isaac's life was spared,
> to show us that God values our lives.
> We thank you for God's Son, Jesus,
> who loved us, and died for us.   Amen.

Hymn:

> Go tell it on the mountain. (C&P. 1. 24)

Teachers' Note: (1) Abraham really loved his son, Isaac. A sacrifice is giving up, something which we love very much. (2) The point is that Abraham was willing to obey God's test, although to us, it seemed to be a very cruel test. (3) This story reminds us of Jesus, who was God's beloved Son, because he was killed on the cross. See John Chapter 3. verse 16.

(a) Andrew Carnegie Millionaire   *Week 4   God's good ideas*

Andrew Carnegie was a Scots boy, who was born in Dunfermline. Near his home was the very beautiful Pittencrief Glen. Andrew loved to see the birds singing, in the trees and bushes. He loved to quietly watch the rabbits nibbling in the long grass. All over the Glen, little Andy could see the wild flowers growing.

It is true to say that little Andy really loved the natural beauty of Pittencrief Glen. He knew that it belonged to a land-owner, and that he was only a poor boy. Andy made up his mind that one day, he would like to buy the Glen, not for himself, but for all the people of Dunfermline to enjoy. Of course, Andrew was only a poor child, and most people would say that he was day-dreaming.

He went to the school in Dunfermline, until he was thirteen years old. Andy was very hungry for knowledge, but being a poor family, they really did not own books of their own. They had the family Bible, but that was all. Andrew used to think to himself, "If only I could have books to read, I would share them with others. Maybe, one day, I will be a rich man, and I will use my riches to buy books for everyone to read." Of course, if anyone had been able to read Andrew's thoughts, they would have said that he was day-dreaming again.

Andrew's parents decided to emigrate to the United States of America, in search of a better way of life. They set sail for America, leaving their beloved Scotland behind them. Andrew began a new way of life in Pittsburg with his parents, who found work in a cotton factory.

Andrew soon found a job as a telegraph messenger boy and began to earn real wages. Sadly, after seven years, his father fell ill, and died. Andrew had grown up to be a young man of twenty years of age. He had to earn enough wages to feed and clothe his younger brother, and his mother, as well as himself.

He had a good brain, and he had taught himself railway telegraphy. The telegraph was a little machine, which used Morse Code. (Dots and dashes). The sounds were tapped out, like a buzzer, and were carried by electricity along the high telegraph wires which were placed beside the railway tracks. So messages could travel much faster that a railway engine. The Station Master on one station could speak to the next station down the line, to tell them whether the train would be late or early, just by asking his Telegraph Operator to tap out the message. Any urgent message could be sent by telegraph, not just railway messages.

Andrew learnt this way of communicating, and he became a Telegraph Operator. His quick brain revealed him to be a good manager. In a short time they made Andrew a Superintendent in the Pennsylvanian Railway Company. Andrew was very good at using money. He bought shares in a Railway company that had the new idea to run sleeping-carriages, for passengers going on long journeys. Andrew made a lot of money, and he became a rich man.

Then Andrew used his money to buy land which had oil underneath it. He sold the oil, and made a lot more money. Now he was very rich. He caused a great iron and steel works to be built in the city of Pittsburg. He became one of the richest men in America. The little Scot's boy had done well in America. Soon he sold all his business interests, and then he retired with a fortune of 500 Million Dollars.

Andrew Carnegie believed that people who make lots of money quickly, should use it in their life-time to share with other people's needs. So he began to give his money to good schools for poor people. He helped to provide Welfare help for training poor Americans.

Andrew remembered that he was British. He also remembered that when he was a little poor boy, that he had very few books to read. He gave more of his money to pay for the building of 2,500 new Free Libraries in cities all over Britain and Ireland. He gave more money to the four Universities of Scotland.

Andrew remembered his childhood in Dunfermline, where he played in the beautiful Pittencrief Glen. He gave more money to buy the Glen from the land-owner. Soon the Glen was made into a Public Park for everyone to enjoy.

People remember Andrew Carnegie as the poor Scots boy, who became a millionaire, and shared his money with other people. He became rich. He provided work for the unemployed, and steel and oil for industry. He was not selfish because he gave his money away again. So Andrew Carnegie's dreams came true. What better way is there to live, than to help other people?

Prayer:

>Lord, we thank you for Andrew Carnegie.
>We thank you for his life, and his skills.
>We admire his kind generosity.
>We remember the words of Jesus,
>It is more blessed to give than to receive.
>Take away all selfishness from us.   Amen.

Hymn:

>For the beauty of the earth. (C&P. 1. 11) or (J.P. 48)

Teachers' Note: (1) Andrew Carnegie began as a very poor boy. Poor children loved the Glens, and green fields and hedges, because the air was pure and fresh. (2) Andrew had two good advantages. He had a quick brain, and a generous heart. (3) Andrew had a deep interest in sharing his good fortune with other people. This is one of God's good ideas, taught by the Lord Jesus.

(b) The Mustard Tree   *Week 4   God's good ideas*

Jesus told the story of a man who took some mustard seed. This seed was very small, almost as small as powder. The man planted this tiny seed in his field. The tiny seed grew secretly, and silently, in the ground, until after several years, it became a Mustard tree about twelve metres tall. The birds of the sky perched on the mustard tree, because they liked to eat the tiny little seeds, which grew on the tree.

Jesus said that the Kingdom of God is like a mustard tree. Jesus meant that God's good ideas often begin in a very small way at first, but they grow, and they soon become widely known It reminds us that nothing seems smaller than an idea in someone's mind. Yet an idea, can grow, and become very useful indeed. Jesus taught that God's good idea was "Christian Love." It grows most surely, just as a mustard seed grows.

The year 1937 was the Coronation year for King George the Sixth and Queen Mary. There was once a girl named Lucy, aged 10 years of age, who was on holiday at a coastal town. Lucy was standing in the Public park. She heard the local band playing stirring music in the bandstand, which was an open-sided building in the middle of the park. A crowd of Town Councillors had gathered. Lucy went closer to watch the proceedings.

The local Mayor and Mayoress were standing, and both were holding brand new shiny spades. Someone had dug a hole in the green, near the band-stand. The Park Gardener was holding a young Sycamore tree. With great care, the Gardener planted the tree in the hole. The Mayor and the Mayoress each put three spadefulls of soil, into the hole. The band played the National Anthem. The Town Councillors shook hands with each other, and the Ceremony was over. The Sycamore tree had been planted to commemorate the Coronation of King George and Queen Mary. Later the Gardener put more soil into the hole, and bedded the young tree firmly down.

Many years passed by. Lucy grew up to be a young woman, and moved away to another part of the country. She married, and raised a family. When they had grown up and left home, she decided to visit the coastal town again with her husband for a short holiday. As she was walking past the Public Park, Lucy, now an older woman, remembered the day in 1937, when she had watched the Mayor and Mayoress plant the tree beside the bandstand.

Lucy decided to look in the park to see if the little tree was still there. Imagine her surprise, when she could see no trace of a little tree. Instead, she saw a huge Sycamore tree, with great thick branches growing up into the sky. There were railings around the tree, and a metal plate with an inscription on it. She read the words, ***"This tree was planted on the 12th. May 1937, by the Mayor and Mayoress of this Borough, in commemoration of the Coronation of King George the Sixth, and Queen Mary."***

Lucy realised that she was no longer a girl of ten years of age. She was now a Grandmother. She noticed that the bandstand had been removed, because of vandalism. Indeed there were not many people in the Public Park. Everything seemed to have changed.

She remembered the story, told by Jesus, about the Mustard Tree. She thought to herself, *"The things which never change are God's good ideas." She remembered the words of the Apostle Paul. "And now remains these three, faith, hope and love, and the greatest of these is LOVE."*

Prayer:

> Lord, we thank you for the story of the Mustard tree,
> which reminds us of the Kingdom of God.
> We praise you for the Lord Jesus,
> who taught us the good ideas of God.
> We pray for faith, and hope,
> but most of all, we pray for Christian Love.   Amen.

Hymn:

> Carpenter, carpenter, make me a tree. (C&P. 1. 5)

Teachers' Note: (1) The Mustard seed was very small, but it grew into a large tree. It is a common saying, "Great oaks grow from small acorns." This means that children may become important people, and that God's seemingly small good ideas have the power to change the world. (2) Time makes changes in everything, even in school. (3) The most powerful thing in the world is Christian love.

(c) Sharing with Others   *Week 4   God's Good Ideas*

The Temple in Jerusalem was a holy building used by the Jews for the worship of God. Near the Courtyard of the women, was the gate named "The Beautiful Gate." Jesus sat close by this gate, and watched the people going into the Temple. The people as they went in to worship, used to put their money offerings into one of the thirteen collecting boxes which were there. The money was used to pay for various needy causes, such as a poor fund, or the Temple expenses.

The rich people were able to put large sums of money into the money boxes, but not everyone in Jerusalem was rich. A poor woman came along. Her husband had died, so there was no wage-earner in her house. She had only two thin coins (leptons) left in her pocket. The coins were worth less than one penny. When the widow came to the collecting box, she put in both coins.

Jesus said to his disciples, "This poor woman has given more than anyone else. Everyone gave into the treasury what they could afford, but she has given every penny she had." It was true, that she had only two coins, but she gave everything. The other rich people might have given more money than she did, but they always had something left. The widow woman had nothing left.

When you come to think about this story, this poor lady could easily have kept back one coin for herself. Jesus commended her an an example of true generosity. Now, this does not mean that God wants you to give away all of your pocket-money. The story is told to show that often it is poor people who share with others.

Old Mary lived a large American city. She was once a beautiful young lady, and lived in her own apartment in a high building. Mary had a good job. She was very happy. After some years, one sad day, Mary fell very ill, and she could not go back to her employment. She was not earning any wages, yet she had to pay the Doctor and hospital bills.

She gradually used up all her savings. After some time passed, she could no longer pay the weekly rent, so she had to give up her apartment. The only place where she could find a small room was in a communal lodging house for vagrants or tramps. Mary stayed there until she became well again. Then she started to work once more. Soon she was able to rent another apartment, and set up her home again.

Mary never forgot the poor people, or the tramps. She remembered the people known as "hoboes" who move about America, hiding in railway waggons. Many evenings she would go round the local bakery shops before closing time. Mary would ask the bakers for boxes of bread which had not been bought that day. The shopkeepers would give her large cardboard boxes of unsold bread.

Mary would take these loaves, and buns home with her. Next day she would go down town and look in the Parks, and public places to find the hungry tramps, and homeless people. She would distribute the bread free of charge to anyone who needed it.

When people asked her why she acted in this way, she always answered that she had read in the Bible, that when Jesus met the five thousand hungry people, he performed a miracle. He told the people to sit down on the green grass. Then he gave them bread to eat. Mary said, "I cannot perform any miracles, but I can share what I have, with people who are hungry." Sharing with other people is one of God's good ideas. Of course, the Police always watched that Mary was kept safe.

Children must not try to help older people who are hungry except by donations to charity of course. Some people might be strangers and might harm them. That kind of sharing work is a special job for specially trained people. Some churches have "Soup Kitchens" where trained workers share out free soup to homeless people after it is dark. Other Churches provide fold- away beds and blankets to homeless people for the night in a church hall.

Children can help in the God's good work of sharing, by taking part in organised Charity events, but always with adults as leaders in charge. A much more difficult decision is to share some of our pocket money with a good cause, such as a children's hospice, or overseas aid to third world countries.

Prayer:

Lord, teach us not to be selfish.
Teach us that it is better to give, than to receive.
Help us to share what we have with others,
who are less fortunate than we are.
Bless all the homeless people.
Bless our school, our teachers,
and every worker.   Amen.

Hymn:

There's a child in the streets. (C&P. 1. 27)

Teachers' Note: (1) Jesus commended the widow woman, because she gave everything she had. Today, we do not need to give away everything that we own, because our people and Government provide financial help, and houses, for poorer people. (That is why people pay taxes). (2) Sharing with others is another of God's good ideas. (3) The third world is a very poor and needy world. Money goes to train people to help themselves.

(a) Telemachus

Week 5   Opportunity

Many of us have been to a football match, or a rugby game, held in a large sports arena. After the match is over, the crowd goes home. The supporters of both sides cheer, sing, and shout a lot. They wave their scarves, maybe, they paint their faces, but after all it is only a game. If someone was hurt, we may be sure that it was just an accident.

Long ago in the City of Rome they also had a great arena. Although the Roman State was supposed to be a Christian State, the rulers allowed the Roman games to kill people for sport. Eighty thousand supporters used to watch the games. Instead of playing football or rugby, they had many strong Gladiators who fought each other. The Gladiators used swords, spears, javelins, and three pronged spears called "tripons." They fought each other, as if they were in a battle.

The crowds sat and watched their favourite Gladiators fight each other. When one Gladiator was stronger than another one, he would, maybe, knock the sword from his opponent's hand. Then he would point his sword at his opponent's heart. It was a horrible sport of killing each other.

The crowd sitting in the arena, would yell and cheer their champion. If the crowd wanted to see one of the Gladiators kill the other Gladiator lying on the ground, then they would shout, "Kill, Kill." The spectators would turn their thumbs down. Their champion would stab his opponent with his sword.

If the crowd thought that both men had fought well, they might cheer, and hold their thumbs up. Their champion, then would not kill his opponent. He would put away his sword in his sheath. They left the arena, prepared to kill or be killed on some other occasion. The Christian people felt that the Roman Games were horrific. No one should be wounded or killed for the sake of sport. Christians would not even attend the games.

Living away in the desert, there was a Christian hermit, by the name of Telmachus. He was a good Christian. He prayed to God that he might be shown a way to stop these horrible killings in the arena. Telemachus travelled to Rome. When he arrived the arena was crowded with people. The Gladiators were fighting and killing each other in teams.

Talemachus jumped down from his seat, and ran across the arena, and stood between the two teams of Gladiators. He was thrown aside by the strong fighters. The crowd were very angry, that someone was spoiling their sport. They shouted, "Go away stranger." Telemachus refused to leave the area, but kept standing between the fighters. "You are all children of God. You should not kill God's children," he shouted.

The Prefect in charge, shouted out an order, and quickly, one of the Gladiators plunged his sword into Telemachus. Immediately, Telemachus fell down dead. The crowd in the seats around the arena, became very quiet. They realised that a good Christian man lay dead on the ground. A silence came over the Games. People began to leave their seats, and to go home. No-one really understood what had happened that day. However, from that day forward, the Gladitorial Games of killing were never held in Rome again.

Telemachus took his opportunity. He had given his life, to stop the killing games, because he believed that we are all God's people, and that we should love each other.

Prayer:

> Heavenly Father, we remember the bravery
> of the Christian hermit, Telemachus.
> We realise that many Christians became Martyrs
> for their faith in Jesus.
> Lord, grant that we may love each other.
> Teach us, like Jesus, to return good for evil.   Amen.

Hymn:

He who would valiant be. (C&P. 1. 44) or (J.P. 80)

Teachers' Note: (1) Christians and many others cannot bear cruelty to others on a sports field. (2) This attitude is held by Christians, because Jesus taught us to love each other. (3) Telemachus by his Christian life and cruel death, caused the Roman killing Games to cease.

(b) A chance to say, "Sorry"   *Week 5   Opportunity*

Many years ago, before engines were invented, there were no cars, buses, trains nor aeroplanes. Ordinary people travelled the roads, either on foot, or on horse-back, or perhaps, by a coach or a cart. The roads were not tar-macadamed, as they are today. Many roads were just dirt-tracks. If there was a Toll-House at the end of a road, the coach-driver had to pay a penny to travel down that road. The money which coach-drivers paid at the Toll House was used to pay the roadmenders, who filled in the holes in the roads with stones and sand.

This particular road that went through the village, was not a Toll Road. This meant that it was more like a dirt track going four different directions. When it rained, it was full of holes and large puddles. Walter was a boy aged eleven. He was bored with himself one dark evening. He went down to the sign-post, showing the four ways; to London, to York, to Epworth, and Doncaster.

He shook the post until it became loose. Walter pulled it out of the damp ground, and turned the signs around to point in another direction. He laughed to himself, and then he slipped away into the darkness.

That night, Mrs. Robert's little baby daughter fell very ill, and they had to send a message to the new Doctor who lived next to the Vicarage, in the village. "Please, come to Robert's farm, as our baby is very ill." The new Doctor, brought out his little pony and trap. He put an oil lamp, at the side of the little cart, and off he went into the darkness, to attend the sick baby.

It was a dark night, without any moon. The new Doctor did not know the district very well. He stopped at the sign-post, and looked for the sign pointing to Epworth. He held his storm light up to read the sign. The Doctor said "Gee up!" and his pony trotted away. The Doctor did not know that a foolish boy had changed the direction of the sign-post. The road he had taken was full of holes, and the wheel of the little cart went down into a deep rut. The cart over-turned in the darkness, and the Doctor was thrown into the hedge. He had to take the frightened horse home, without the cart. He realised that he had taken the wrong road to Robert's farm.

When he arrived back at the sign-post, Mr. Roberts was standing in the darkness. He guided the Doctor to his farm-house. The Doctor found that the baby had colic, causing the baby's tummy pains. He prescribed, magnesia in a bottle for the baby. Mrs. Roberts poured two spoonfuls into the baby's mouth, and it soon stopped crying. The Doctor went home. Next morning, the Villagers found that the signpost had been moved to point in the wrong direction. No one ever knew who had moved the sign-post.

Six months afterwards, Walter felt very guilty, because he knew that he was to blame for everything that had happened that awful night. The baby might have died, or the pony might have broken its leg. Worse still, the new Doctor might have broken his neck, and been killed, when he had been thrown out into the hedge.

Walter broke out in spots, and he became very itchy. His mother sent him to see the Doctor. Walter was terrified, but he had to go. The Doctor welcomed Walter, and spoke very kindly to him. He looked at his itchy spots, and gave him a lotion to rub on them. He was so gentle and understanding, that Walter felt more guilty than ever. The Doctor said to Walter, "Now Son, there is something troubling you very much. Would you like to tell me about it.?"

Walter realised that at last he had an opportunity to get rid of the awful guilty feelings hc had. Evcry night hc used to dream of the pony and trap falling down in the darkness on the wrong road. In his dreams he could hear a baby crying. Walter knew that his opportunity had come. "Doctor, I want to tell you that I am very sorry for all the harm I caused. It was me, who changed the sign post to point in the wrong direction." Then Walter began to cry as if he could not stop.

The new Doctor put his arm around the boy. He said, "Walter, I will forgive you, and I shall never tell anyone about what happened here tonight." Walter stopped crying. He felt relieved inside himself. He had felt so wicked for six long months. The Doctor said to Walter, "When you say your prayers tonight, tell God that you are sorry. Ask God to forgive you. Then, go downstairs and wash your hands which did the wrong deed in the wash-tub, as a sign to yourself that you will never do such a bad deed ever again. In the morning, you will find that everything will be different."

That evening, Walter went home, and said his prayers, asking God to forgive him. Afterwards he washed his hands which did the wrong deed. Next morning when he awoke, he really did feel different. He was happy again. and would you believe it, his itchy spots had disappeared during the night!

Prayer:

Lord teach that when we foolishly do wrong,
to ask God's forgiveness. and mercy.
May we have clean hands and a pure heart.

Teach us that true happiness
comes from a clear conscience.
Bless our school, and every pupil.   Amen.

Hymn:

Father hear the prayer we offer. (C&P. 1. 48)

Teachers' Note: (1) Walter did not realise that his foolish prank could have hurt others. (Doctor, pony, or the little baby). (2) When we do wrongful actions, they may torment us in our consciences. (3) Walter found relief by telling the Doctor, and by saying his prayers. There is a text to be found in the Psalms, "Who shall ascend into the hill of the Lord, or who shall stand in his holy place. He/she who has clean hands (actions) and a pure heart." (Psalm 24 v 4.)

(c) Five wise and five foolish girls   *Week 5   Opportunity*

Jesus told the story about a Bride's ten girl-friends. The Bride was just about to be married. The wedding was to be held in a Jewish village. The custom was for the Bridegroom to come to the Bride's house on the evening of the wedding. The wedding celebrations afterwards went on for several days.

The ten girl friends were expected to visit the Bride's home, and to stay with her, until the Bridegroom arrived. It was a custom that the visitors to the house all carried oil-lamps, which were lighted during the evening. These small lamps had a wick of thin rope in them The oil-soaked wick was set alight. It burned, and gave good light to those who carried them. As you can imagine, lamps were very important in days when there was no electricity.

The ten girls all had arrived at the Bride's home that evening, when five of them discovered that their already lighted oil-lamps were going out. They all carried oil jars along with them, to refill their lamps with oil. However, the five girls whose lamps were going out, discovered that the oil jars which they had been carrying, were empty.

Just then, a call was heard in the darkness of the village street. Someone was calling out loudly, "Look, the Bridegroom is coming. Go out and meet him." Five of the wise girls who had oil in their lamps, lighted the wicks of their lamps, and went out in the darkness to meet the Bridegroom. The five foolish girls who had run short of oil, said to the five wise girls, "Lend us some of your oil, that we may also go to meet the Bridegroom."

The five wise girls replied, "No we are very sorry, but we cannot give you any oil from our oil-jars, because there is only enough oil for one lamp each. You, five girls, had better go to the shop, and buy some more oil for your own use."

Off the five foolish girls went in the darkness to find the shop. While they were away, the Bridegroom arrived outside the Bride's house. He went inside. The five wise girls followed him inside to the wedding celebrations.

It was a strict rule in those days, that when the door was shut, the wedding celebrations could begin. No-one was allowed in late, in case they disturbed the wedding. By the time the five foolish girls had bought more oil at the shop, and returned, they of course, had been locked out.

The door was shut. "The five foolish girls called out, "Sir, Please open the door." The Bridegroom answered them as they stood outside in the darkness, "This is the truth, I do not know you." The five foolish girls had to go away home. They had left matters too late! They never enjoyed seeing the Bride and Bridegroom being married. Jesus, after telling this story, said, "Be on your watch, for you do not know the importance of the day, nor the hour."

The meaning of the story was, that the people had been waiting to meet the Messiah, whom God had promised, was to come to them. Jesus was the Messiah whom God had sent, but the people did not go out to welcome him. He had already come, and they were too late.

We must try never to be late. There are many happenings in life that depend on us arriving on time. The train will not wait for you. A school examination will not wait for you. Many people say that they will be better people some day in the future, but they forget that life goes past very quickly. They become old people before they realise it. So we know that the clock or the calender will not wait for us. We must be ready to take the opportunities of life, when they come. Every day brings an opportunity to pray to God.

Prayer:

    Father we thank you for life.
    We thank you for every new day
    Teach us to use up every hour,
    and to enjoy every moment.
    When the important events of life arrive,
    help us not to be late to welcome them.   Amen.

Hymn:

    Give me oil in my lamp. (C&P. 1. 43) or (J.P. 50)

Teachers' Note: (1) Did you notice that all ten girls had good intentions? They all were very sincere in wanting to attend the wedding. (2) Five of the girls were wise, because they had prepared for the wedding, by bringing oil to make their lamps burn brightly. (3) Five of the girls were foolish because they had not really thought about preparing for the wedding by buying oil, for their lamps. Light was very important for an evening Jewish wedding. Maybe all of us are divided into two classes. Those who like to prepare, and those who do not. Reference: Matthew Chapter 25 v.1-13.

(a) The angel in the stone   *Week 6   Imagination*

There was once an Italian sculptor, who ordered a huge piece of marble from the stone quarry. After some time, the enormous stone was delivered to the sculptor's workshop. It had been carried on a low cart, with small wheels, and drawn by a team of strong horses.

The sculptor began to carve his statue from the marble, knocking a piece of stone off here and there. He worked on the stone for several weeks. One morning he noticed a flaw in the stone. There was a crack in the marble, which he had never noticed before. He realised that the marble was no longer of any use to him for making his statue. The stone was moved out of the work-shop, on to some waste ground nearby. There it lay for a long time.

Michelangelo, a famous painter, engineer, and sculptor happened to see the huge piece of cracked marble lying outside the work-shop. He looked at the stone, and then he stared at it.: He continued to look at the marble, as if he was looking right down inside the stone, but of course, you cannot look inside stone. Really, he was using his imagination. He imagined that that he could see an angel, in the stone. Michelangelo bought the stone from the first sculptor who considered it to be flawed and of no use.

Michaelangelo had the stone moved to his own workshop. Soon, he began to chisel pieces out of the stone, until gradually, as he worked, it took the form of a beautiful angel. When the sculpture was finished, no-one could believe that the angel had been chiselled out of the rejected marble. It was Michelangelo's deep imagination, and skill which had created the angel.

There is something good in everyone of us. Inward good character is like the angel in the stone. When Youth Leaders help a bad boy or girl to become a good boy or girl, they help to bring out the angel in them. Jesus could see the angel in everyone. He once helped Zacchaeus, a little Tax-collector who was a dishonest person. The tax-collector had climbed up a sycamore tree, because he was small in stature, and could not see over the heads of the crowd. Jesus went to Zacchaeus' house for a meal.

The little man believed in Jesus. He became a changed person. He gave the money back to the people he had robbed. After Zacchaeus believed in Jesus, he became a generous man, giving his money to help poor people. It all began when Jesus had the imagination to see the good in the little tax-collector. If you have faith, then you always have good imagination.

Prayer:

Lord, today, we thank you,
for the imagination of faith.
Help us to see good in everyone.
May our teachers have good imagination,
and see good in every pupil in our school.   Amen.

Hymn:

My faith it is an oaken staff. (C&P. 1. 46)

Teachers' Note: (1) Everyone is like the stone in the story. Not one of us is perfect. We all have faults. (2) It takes someone with faith to look at us with good imagination, and to see what we could be in the future. (3) Jesus always had the ability to see the best in people.

(b) The Life-boat-man's daughter   *Week 6   Imagination*

It was because seamen could imagine what it is like to be on a sinking vessel, that they joined the Life-boat service and risked their own lives. Imagination is a good thing, when it helps us to see the suffering of other people. Then, we do not want to think selfishly about saving ourselves, while others are in danger. We are now going to imagine just what it was like, to be the daughter of a life-boat-man.

Little Peggy's father was a life-boat- man. Peggy lived near the seaside town of Lytham in Lancashire. Lytham had its own life-boat. It was simply a large rowing boat, lined with cork. The cork was to make the lifeboat buoyant in stormy waters.

The crew who were dressed in South-Westers, and oilskin coats and trousers, pulled the oars together, as there was no engine in the life-boats in those days. Peggy used to be afraid that her Dad might go out in the life-boat in a storm, and the sea might be so rough, that the life-boat might overturn. She always prayed to God that her Dad would come home safely again.

Peggy's Dad was just like all the other life-boat-men. They were good God-fearing sea-men, and all very brave, but they never boasted about being brave. They did not fear the sea, they simply had a deep respect for it. They just hoped that they would be in time, to rescue drowning people from a sinking ship.

It was the year 1886. On the 9th. of December, the rocket flare went up into the sky, calling out the crew of the Lytham lifeboat. There was a fearful storm blowing in the Preston Estuary. A German ship, named, "Mexico" had been trying to reach the harbour at Preston, but had been driven by the gale on to the sands on the Hesketh side of the Estuary. There were twelve men in the German ship, and it was likely that they all would be drowned in the stormy sea, if they were not rescued quickly.

Little Peggy watched her Dad rush down to the sea with other members of the crew. The wind was blowing strongly and they had difficulty in launching the life-boat. The life-boat at Southport, and the lifeboat at St. Annes also had been launched that stormy day.

Peggy did not know then, but both the St. Anne's life-boat, and the Southport lifeboat later had capsized. Twenty-seven brave life-boat-men lost their lives in the stormy waters. However, the Lytham crew rowed their life-boat across the troubled waters to the "Mexico." Despite the raging wind, they managed to save all twelve crew-men from the German boat. They brought the twelve rescued men back in their life-boat to safety on shore.

Peggy and her mother watched as the brave life-boat men returned, tired, but pleased that they had saved twelve lives. Peggy threw her arms around her Dad, and said, "Welcome home, Dad." She asked her father, "Why do you risk your life trying to save other seamen?" Dad replied, "Peggy, I cannot imagine sitting beside a warm fireside, when a ship has been wrecked, and is lying near Lytham." Peggy thought to herself, what a strange thing imagination is. It produces action .

As Peggy said her prayers that night, she thanked God for the safe return of her Dad, and for his unselfish imagination.

Prayer:

Father, God, we thank you
for the brave life-boat men.
Bless their wives and families.
May our own imagination spur us on
to do brave and kind actions,
    that will truly help other people.   Amen.

Hymn:

Waves are beating on the shore. (C&P. 2. 84)

Teachers' Note: (1) "Imagination" is seeing events in our minds. Imagination helps us to order and control our actions. (2) The Life-boat-men were courageous to go out on dangerous stormy seas in a rowing boat. (3) The families of the life-boat-men often belong to churches near the jetty. This is where they found their faith and good imagination.

(c) James' story   *Week 6   Imagination*

Some of the Bible stories are very short. We do not know how they really ended. It is like watching a film on the television, we all wonder whatever happened, after the words, "THE END" appears on the screen.

Some people have a good imagination. This means seeing a picture in your mind of what is not actually there. It is a bit like a day-dream. You could not be an artist, or an actor, unless you have imagination. Indeed, you could not be an architect or a sculptor unless you had some imagination. Nor could you be a poet. You certainly could not be a good sports-person, unless you can imagine yourself winning. Of course, there is also such a thing as bad imagination.

The Headteacher's story

James' Headteacher decided to test his imagination. He himself told the first part of a Bible story, and James had to finish the story using his own imagination. Listen now to the Headteacher's story, and then to how James finished it.

"One Sabbath day, Jesus was in the Jewish Synagogue at a Jewish Church service. Now, in those days, the strict Jews never worked on the Sabbath day. Jesus the healer, happened to notice that there was a man attending the service who had a paralysed hand.

The Pharisees (Religious Leaders) who were trying to find faults, asked Jesus, "Is it right to heal on the Sabbath day?" Jesus replied, "If any of you see one of his sheep fall into a pit on the Sabbath day, will you not pull it out? Surely, a man is more valuable than a sheep. It is always lawful to do good on the sabbath day."

Then Jesus said to the man with the paralysed hand, "Stretch forth your hand."

As the man obeyed Jesus, and as he moved his hand outwards, he was healed instantly. One hand became just as useful as the other hand. The Pharisees were angry, and went away. The Headteacher had finished his story.

James' Story

James began. "I like to imagine that the people in Bible stories were just like people today.

The man with the withered hand was called "Josiah." Ever from Josiah was a little boy he always wanted to be a drummer in the village band. However, because he had a paralysed hand, he knew that he could never be a drummer. He used to watch the village band walk up the street, as it went off to play at weddings or funerals. Sometimes, the band led the worshippers up the hill to the Temple at the feast time. Josiah was a handicapped person, who loved music.

He had tried to get a job when he was older, but no-one wanted a person with a paralysed hand in those days, so Josiah was never able to find a job. Nevertheless, Josiah believed in God, and went to the Synagogue every sabbath day. When Jesus the healer cured his paralysed hand, Josiah was the happiest person in the village.

Josiah joined the village band, and found that the more he practised beating the drum, the stronger his hand became. Then the musicians allowed Josiah to become the Band Major. He was allowed to lead the band as it marched down the village street. He carried a beautiful silver staff with red and yellow tassles hanging from it. Josiah looked magnificent leading the village band.

One day as the band was marching along past the market, Jesus was standing at the corner. Jesus recognised Josiah as the man whom he had healed. In turn, Josiah recognised Jesus as the healer. Josiah thought to himself, "How can I show Jesus just how well I feel." Then he remembered that he was now the Band Major.

He took hold of his silver staff, with the red and yellow tassle hanging from it. As the band was marching, and playing a rousing tune, Josiah threw his Major's silver staff high up into the air. Jesus watched him, and wondered whether Josiah would be able to catch it, as it turned over and over in the air.

Josiah now had a steady eye, and a strong hand. As the Major's staff fell downwards, Josiah stretched out his hand and caught it, and then he gave it another twirl. He heard Jesus shout "Bravo Josiah. Good catch!" As the band went marching up the village street, both Josiah and Jesus looked and smiled at each other."

At this point, James had run out of breath, so he had to stop. The teachers, the Head teacher, and the children at first sat in silence. They thought James' ending to the story had been a brilliant ending, and very helpful too!. They just clapped their hands, and shouted in the Assembly, "Bravo James! "

Prayer:

O God, our Heavenly Father,
We pray for all handicapped people.
Bless them, and help them to achieve success
in whatever they are trying to do.
We thank you for health and strength.
Make us all patient and kind towards others.   Amen.

Hymn:

I saw the man from Galilee. (C&P. 2. 75)

Teachers' Note: (1) The Christian Sabbath is Sunday, the first day of the week. The Jewish Sabbath is the seventh day,(Saturday). They are special days useful for worship, rest, recreation, and doing good. (2) Jesus completely healed the man with the paralysed hand. (3) James' imagination put a good ending to the story. Perhaps, children in the Worship Assembly could imitate James, and later in class, write a short ending for this story. Reference; Matthew 12 v 9-14.

(a) King Arthur's Sword

There are many ancient stories and legends told about King Arthur. Often they became joined together, as they were repeated from person to person, down the years.

A fierce battle had ended, and many soldiers had been killed. The good King Arthur had been deeply wounded. The last living soldier of the Knights of the Round Table happened to be Sir Bedevere. He was King Arthur's trusted friend. King Arthur realised that his own death was near. He possessed a wonderful sword, named "Excalibur." King Arthur called his friend, Sir Bedevere, to his side, and commanded him to take his sword, "Excalibur," and to throw it into the middle of the lake.

This was the sword, which many years before, when Arthur was a young man, had been embedded in a stone. No-one could pull the sword out of the stone. Many soldiers and Knights had tried to do so, but nobody had succeeded. Then young Arthur came along. He was a good man, with a pure heart.

He attempted to pull the sword, and in his hands, the sword easily came out of the stone. Arthur became King, and one hundred brave knights joined his band of soldiers. The famous band of soldiers became known as, "The Knights of the Round Table".

Now, the good King Arthur was dying. His friend, Sir Bedevere carried the sword, named "Excalibur," to the reeds growing around the sides of the lake. It was in the evening, and the Winter moon was shining down on the handle of the sword. The sword handle being studded with diamonds and other precious jewels glistened and sparkled in the moonlight.

However, Sir Bedevere could not bring himself to part with such a precious and famous sword, by throwing it into the middle of the lake. Instead, he secretly hid the sword among the reeds. When he arrived back, King Arthur asked Sir Bedevere, what he had seen and heard. Sir Bedevere answered that he had seen flowing water, and heard the river washing against the rocks. King Arthur knew that his friend had disobeyed his command, and that he was telling lies. Sir Bedevere had kept the sword for himself.

King Arthur commanded him a second time, to go, and to throw Excalibur into the middle of the lake. Sir Bedevere thought to himself, "Maybe the king is sick, and does not really know what he is doing?" He returned to the lake. He handled the sword, but once more, he decided to keep it for himself. Again, hid the sword in the reeds, and came back to King.

King Arthur asked, "What have you seen, and what have you heard?" Sir Bedevere answered again, "I have seen the flowing water, and heard the river washing against the rocks." King Arthur knew that his friend had not obeyed him, but that he had kept the sword, and hidden it somewhere. Sir Bedevere was amazed that King could know, that the sword had not been thrown into the lake.

King Arthur was angry. For a third time, he ordered his friend to go, and to throw Excalibur into the lake. This time, Sir Bedevere obeyed. He stood at the water's edge, and three times, he swirled the jewelled sword around his head, and then he threw Excalibur far out into the lake.

While the sword was in the air, an arm clothed in white, appeared from out of the water. The hand caught the sword, and waved it around three times, and then slowly took the sword below the moonlit waters of the lake. Sir Bedevere saw it happen. He ran back to tell King Arthur.

Arthur said to his friend, before he had spoken, "Now I see by your eyes that you have obeyed my command. Tell me what you saw." Sir Bedevere told the dying king, about the arm clothed in white, which appeared out of the water, and how it had caught the sword in the air as it fell. King Arthur knew that his friend was telling the truth. This was the sign by which he knew that his life's work as a good king was over.

Soon he knew that he would die, and close his eyes for ever. He asked his friend to pray for him. Sir Bedevere wept as a barge carried King Arthur away across the waters to the happy island valley of Avilion. So ends the ancient story of the death of King Arthur, which you may read for yourself, when you are older.

Prayer:

> Heavenly Father, we thank you for the old legend
> of King Arthur, and the Knights of the Round Table.
> Teach us to read stories that show us,
> how to be good, kind, and pure-hearted.
> May we also read the Bible,
> and learn about our Lord Jesus.   Amen.

Hymn:

> When a knight won his spurs. (C&P. 1. 50)

Teachers' Note: (1) King Arthur had a trusted friend in Sir Bedevere. It is always a happy experience to have someone we may trust as a real friend. (2) Sir Bedevere was tempted to keep the jewelled sword for himself. On the third occasion, his love for his King was stronger than his desire to keep the sword. (3) The old legend about the hand rising out of the water to receive back the sword, Excalibur, implied that Arthur knew that his life's work was finished.

(b) The Feathers   *Week 7   The Unexpected*

Once upon a time there was a good king who had many servants. One of these servants had come from a very poor home. The king had trusted him, and made him a steward over his estate. This was a well paid position, and soon the servant became a very rich man. Yet the steward was not content. He began to tell lies about the King.

Someone told the good king that his honoured steward was spreading lies about him. The king commanded his steward to appear before him. The king commanded his steward to take a large bag of feathers and to spread them all over the countryside.

The Steward went out from the king, and carried the bag out into the country. It was a very windy day, so the steward opened the bag of feathers, and threw handfulls of feathers all round him. Immediately, the wind blew the fathers here, there, and everywhere. They blew across the fields, and they blew up the mountains, and they blew all round the lakeside. They blew down the village streets, and they blew into peoples shops. Feathers stuck to the feet of the cows and horses. Ordinary people had a few feathers stuck to the soles of their shoes.

The steward returned to the king, and said to him, "I am pleased to report that the the bag of feathers has been spread over your kingdom." The King replied, "Now, I command you to go out with the same bag, and you must collect every feather you have spread across the country. Bring all the feathers back to me."

The steward protested to the king. He said, "How can I bring every feather back to you. By this time, the feathers will have been blown to every part of your kingdom. It would be impossible to bring them all back."

The good king, looked at his steward, and said, "Do you not realise that words are like feathers. Once you have told lies, they spread abroad everywhere. After you speak, your words can never be taken back. What lies you have told about me, will have spread to the farthest parts of my kingdom. You, nor anyone else could ever bring them back."

The steward realised how wicked his tongue had become. He thought that he would never be found out. The terrible thing about telling lies, is that once you tell one lie, then you have to keep telling other lies, in order to cover up the first lie which you told.

The king said to his steward, "I now know that I cannot trust you. You shall no longer be my steward. I shall put an honest person in your position. You shall sweep all the roads of my kingdom, until you find every feather." Many years afterwards, an old man could be seen sweeping the roads of the kingdom, but even then, he could not find all the feathers, which he had spread on the first occasion.

All good children should remember that people trust them always to tell the truth.

Prayer:

>Good Lord, you are the God of truth.
>Help us always to be truthful.
>We thank you for Jesus Christ,
>the one who never told a lie.
>Teach us to guard our speech,
>and let our words be kind.   Amen.

Hymn:

>Kum ba yah my Lord, Kum ba yah. (C&P. 1. 68).

Teachers' Note: (1) The king's steward ought to have been thankful and respected his king, because the king had really been his best friend. (2) Sometime we deliberately tell lies about other people. This is evil gossip. (3). The terrible thing about the things we say is that we may never be able to bring the words back again. Therefore, we must never tell lies about anyone.

(c) Perfume   *Week 7   The Unexpected*

One day, Jesus and his twelve disciples were invited to a meal at the house of Simon the Leper, which was in the village of Bethany. Simon had provided a splendid meal. In those days, Jesus and his disciples did not sit on chairs at a table. Instead, there was a very low table, surrounded by low couches. (cushions). Guests at a meal reclined, on the couches. They leaned on their left elbows, so that their right hands would be free to stretch out to the table.

As the meal was proceeding, a woman came into the room. In her hands she carried a very expensive alabaster jar of perfume, (known as 'nard'). In those days, it was the custom to pour a few drops of perfume upon the heads of a guest. Only a few drops were used, because this jar of perfume cost as much as a man might earn in one whole year. It was very expensive perfume.

The woman approached Jesus. She broke open the alabaster jar. Then, she poured the whole of the contents of the jar over the head of Jesus. The room was filled with the lovely scent. Some of those people who were in the room were displeased. They thought that to pour all the perfume over one person was very wasteful. They asked, "Why such a waste of perfume, which cost ten pounds for one jar? Why was this perfume not sold, and the money gained, given to the poor people of the village?"

However, there was another use for this perfume. When anyone died, their friends would pour perfume over the body, and the broken perfume jar was left in the grave. At that moment, no-one was thinking about funerals.

Jesus spoke out to defend the woman. "Leave her alone, because she has done a very beautiful thing to me. You have the poor people with you all the time. Whenever you like, you can always do something for them. You will not have me with you for much longer. This woman has done the best she could. She has anointed me for my burial. In the future, when the Good News is being preached, after I am gone, the whole world will remember her good deed."

Sometimes we do not always understand the results of our own actions until a long time afterwards. No-one knew at that time that Jesus would be killed on a cruel cross. So, the woman's gift was the right thing to do, at that time, because no-one ever poured perfume on the head of Jesus, after he was dead.

There was once, a girl named Hazel, who was going to see her Grandma in hospital, who happened to be very ill. Hazel used her pocket money to buy a big bunch of flowers for her Grandma, because she really loved her. Hazel's Grandma was so pleased to receive the flowers, that she gave Hazel a big hug, before they said "Good Bye."

No-one expected it, but the very next day, Grandma died, and went home to Heaven. Hazel was glad she had spent her money on the bunch of flowers, because she felt that it was better to give flowers to a living person, than to put them on a grave. Hazel acted like the woman with the perfume. Do you agree?

Prayer:

Heavenly Father, we shall always remember
the kind woman who anointed the head of Jesus.
Help each one of us, to behave in such a way,
that other people may remember us,
because we also were kind, and loving.
Bless all sick children.
Through Jesus Christ our Lord.   Amen.

Hymn:

Said Judas to Mary. (C&P. 1. 28)

Teachers' Note: (1) Jesus had many friends, and he enjoyed visiting them. (2) The kind woman at that moment, did not realise the importance of what she was doing. (3) Hazel did not realise the importance of bringing flowers to her Grandma in hospital at that time. Afterwards, she was glad that she had done so.

(a) Echoes

Some time ago, it was the custom to allow children to freely go up mountains alone, or to go for hikes into the country. Once, there were five children out on a picnic. They lived in Belfast, (Northern Ireland), but they were now on holiday. They had been staying for two weeks in a farm house, near the lovely village of Rostrevor in County Down. The children had been allowed to go on a climbing expedition up the mountains of Mourne, to see the famous Cloughmore Stone. This very large rock, had been lying, like a huge egg, on the top of the mountain, for thousands of years. Tourists from all over the world climbed the mountain, just to see the Cloughmore Stone.

The five children started on their climb, by walking through the Fairy Glen at the foot of the mountain. As they steadily ascended the high mountain, they felt that they lived in the most beautiful country in the world. When they stopped for a breath, they looked back and downwards. Sure enough, it was just as the author of of the song, "The Mountains of Mourne" had written. These high mountains really did sweep down to the sea.

It was a beautiful sunny day, and they could see the fishing boats sailing far out in Carlingford Lough. They could see to the end of the Lough as far as Greencastle in Eire. They watched the big ships on the Irish Sea. Far down below them, on their side of the Lough, were the houses of Rostrevor and Warrenpoint. Looking down from the height of the mountain, the houses seemed to be as small as matchboxes.

The children thought it was a magnificent view. They became hungry, so they each opened their sandwiches, curious to see what was inside them. They drank their pop, but they did not throw away their empty cans. They knew how to take care of the environment, by later carrying the cans down again.

They decided to play the "echo game". Each of the children shouted "Echo", and waited, to hear the answer. Somewhere from the mountain side, the sound came back from the rocks and trees, "Echo.. echo.. echo..echo!" ... and then the sound faded away into a long silence. Rosaleen shouted once more, "Echo!" However, this time the result was mysterious and different.

The sound went round the rocks and trees, and back came the answer, Echo..echo..echo..echo.! The children waited for the silence, but instead of the silence, they were very surprised when they heard someone at a distance calling, "Help..help..help..help..!" Then the silence came again. Immediately, the children knew that someone was in trouble. They collected their ruck-sacks, and made their way to where the call for help had come.

Half a mile away, among the trees, a man lay on the ground. He was a climber, who had suffered a heart attack. The children decided that three of them should stay beside the man, who was unconscious. The other two children went for help. Off the two went, moving as quickly as they could, down the mountainside. They rushed through the Fairy Glen, to the main road. There was a public telephone, where they were able to dial 999, and to call for help.

The children waited at the entrance of the path through the Fairy Glen. They were astonished to see one of the new helicopters arrive, like a huge bird coming down from the sky. It came to rest on a grassy area. A door slid open, and the flying ambulance men called the two children to get into the helicopter. The children were a little fearful, as the helicopter took off into the air again. They were able to look through the windows, and to point out the exact place on the mountain, where the injured man lay on the heather. The other three children were still guarding their patient.

The flying ambulance men carefully strapped the patient down to a stretcher, and brought him inside the helicopter. The helicopter rose again into the air, and carried the patient over the tops of the houses, directly to the hospital. The five children made their own way down the mountain. By this time, a crowd of people had gathered to see what was happening.

Next week everyone read about the rescue in the newspaper. On the front page, there were headlines,

"ECHO CHILDREN SAVE LIFE OF MOUNTAINEER."

"Last week, five Belfast children, here on holiday, shouted from the Cloughmore stone, expecting to hear an echo. They heard an echo, alright, but they also heard a cry for help. By their quick action, the life of a famous mountaineer has been saved. The climber had suffered a serious heart attack, when climbing alone. In answer to the the children's telephone call, a flying ambulance helicopter was sent to the rescue. The patient was ferried to hospital in a matter of minutes. These five brave children have saved a man's life. The climber is recovering in hospital."

After their holiday, the five children went home to tell their parents about their adventure. They had used their voices to help someone in great need.

Prayer:

> Lord, we thank you for the human voice.
> We may sing, and cheer, and encourage our team.
> We may sing praises to God in our school Assembly.
> We may say, thank you, for a kindness shown to us.
> We may pray, when we we need a friend.
> Hear our silent, and spoken prayers.   Amen.

Hymn:

Go tell it on the mountain. (C&P. 1. 24) (J.P. 65)

Teachers' Note: (1) Children today should never go up a mountain, unless accompanied by a parent or Youth Leader. Echoes are sounds bouncing off hard surfaces, such as rocks. Empty rooms sometimes have an echo. (2) These children were kind-hearted, and intelligent children. They could easily have left the man lying alone on the mountain, but they did not do this. (3) Can you mention ten uses of the human voice. (Singing, shouting, whispering, gossiping, warning, telling lies, swearing, encouraging, praying, and repeating poetry.)

(b) Bouncer and Basher   *Week 8   The Human Voice*

The two boys from the chicken farm, were called Ralph, and Tony, but the other children called them, outside the school, by nick names. Ralph and Tony were known as Bouncer and Basher, just because they were bullies. They were thoroughly nasty boys, and seemed to delight in causing trouble.

One evening they telephoned the fire brigade, and ambulance service. They told the telephone operator that the school was on fire. The alarm bells rang in the fire station, and the part-time firemen ran to the station to get the fire tender going. The fire crew were very quick, indeed. Soon the fire tender was sounding its siren as it rushed to the school house, followed by an ambulance. Bouncer and Basher were hiding behind the hedge, and having a silly laugh at what was happening. Just at that very moment, Ralph's and Tony's father, who lived several miles along the road, had gone into one of the two long chicken houses on his farm.

He had smelt smoke coming from the electric wires under the buildings. It was a windy day, and the dry floors underneath the chicken house had caught fire, and were burning fiercely. The boy's father did not know that the floor underneath had nearly burned away. Smoke filled the chicken house, and he could not see clearly. As he tried to crawl back out of the chicken-house, the floor gave way. The boy's father felt his leg go though the burning wooden floorboards. He shouted for help. Fortunately, his wife heard him. She ran into the farm house, and phoned 999.

The boy's father, managed to crawl out of the long chicken-house, but he collapsed on the grass, He could hardly breathe, his lungs being filled with fumes and smoke. The fire-crew had by this time reached the school, and they realised that it was a hoax call. The school was not really on fire. Bouncer and Basher sat behind the hedge laughing. They did not realise that this was a sick joke, and a stupid prank to play.

They heard a voice coming over the Fire Officer's radio telephone, loud and clear. The voice said, "Do not return to the fire station. Instead, go immediately, to a fire at Hillside Chicken-Farm, Gray's Lane. The ambulance will follow. Over and out." The Fire Officer, answered on his radio telephone, "Message received, and understood. Over and out." Meanwhile, Bouncer and Basher, realised that Hillside Chicken Farm was their father's farm. They pedalled home on their mountain bikes as fast as they could.

Of course, the fire tender, and the ambulance rushed past them. By the time they had pedalled the two miles, their father had been taken away in the ambulance. The fire crew had their first hosepipe and pump already pouring water on the chicken-house. The big main hosepipe was also being attached quickly to the water main in the road. Soon both hoses were pouring thousands of litres of water on the fire. A second chicken-house nearby, built of very dry wood, had also caught fire.

Eventually, the flames in both chicken-houses were doused with water. They were left two blackened ruins. Worse still, hundreds of chickens had been killed by the smoke, in the two fires.

Bouncer and Basher, were thoroughly ashamed of themselves, because they were soon found out. They had to go before the children's court, and answer for their actions to the magistrates. One of the magistrates spoke from his chair . He said, "What you did that day, was not a joke. It was a crime. There was no fire at your school. You have wasted the fire-crew's time, and cost needless expense.

Your stupid action in wasting the fire-crews and ambulance men's time, might also have cost your own father his life. The fire engine was delayed by your false information, and it took longer to attend the fire. Because it arrived late, a second chicken-house has been burned down, and hundreds of chickens have been killed."

Bouncer and Basher were ashamed of themselves. Both boys apologised to the magistrates. They were truly sorry, and promised that they would be better behaved in future. The school children watched the two boys, and realised that they really were changed characters. No one ever called them "Bouncer" and "Basher" any more. They were now known to everyone as "Ralph" and "Tony".

Prayer:

>Lord, help us to use our voices
>always to speak the truth.
>May our every word be kind and honest.
>Teach us not to tell lies.
>Bless all teachers and children,
>of every language around the world. Amen.

Hymn:
God in his love for us lent us this planet. (C&P. 2. 76)

Teachers' Note: (1) We may use our voices for good or for evil. Bouncer and Basher were actually telling lies over the telephone, when really there was no fire at the school. (2) We may pray for all the people who work in the rescue services. (3) Bouncer and Basher became changed characters, and people now called them by their, "Christian" names, Ralph and Tony.

(c) The Man Who Lost His Voice   *Week 8   The Human Voice*

Mary, the mother of Jesus, had a cousin named Elizabeth. Now, Elizabeth's husband was named Zechariah, On one occasion he lost his voice. Here is the story of how it happened!

Both Zechariah and Elizabeth both longed to have a little baby of their own. They grew older, and no baby ever came. They prayed very much about the matter, but it seemed that they would never have a family. Now, Zechariah was a Jewish priest, who on occasions would take part in the Service at the Temple in Jerusalem. His part was to burn the sweet smelling incense on the Temple altar.

The angel, Gabriel, appeared to Zechariah one day. The angel said, "Zechariah, God has sent me to tell you that he has heard your prayers. You and Elizabeth will have a baby son. You are to call the baby, "John." " In the future, your son, John , will grow up to be a famous person. He will be a joy to the both of you. He will preach to the people, and lead many back to the ways of God. He will be like the Old Testament prophet, Elijah. He will go before the Lord, and prepare the people for the Lord."

Zechariah asked the angel, how he could be sure about this message. The angel said, "I am Gabriel, who stands in the presence of God. Because you do not really believe this message, you will be silent, until the baby is actually born." Zechariah was struck dumb, and he could only make himself understood by signing with his hands. When his time of service was completed, he went home to his wife, Elizabeth. What a shock Elizabeth received to learn that her husband could not speak. He sometimes had to write a message on a writing tablet.

When Elizabeth's baby was born, everyone wanted to know the baby's name. Elizabeth said, "He is to be called, 'John' ". People were surprised, and said, "No one in our family has that name." They made signs to Zechariah, the father of the baby, to find out what the baby should be called. To everyone's surprise, he wrote, "His name is, 'John' " At that very moment God healed Zechariah. His speech came back again. Zechariah used his voice to thank the Lord for his little son. Little baby John later became the famous John the Baptist. .

Prayer:

Heavenly Father, we thank you for Zechariah, the priest.
and for all God's ministers and servants.
We thank you for the two mothers, Mary and Elizabeth.
We thank you for our parents and guardians.
We thank you for the two babies, Jesus and John.
May we use our voices to give praise unto God.   Amen.

Hymn:

Now thank we all our God. (C&P. 1. 38) or (J. P. 175)

Teachers' Note: (1) Note that Zechariah and Elizabeth loved the Lord. (2) Note that God always keeps his promises. A son was really born, despite the older age of the parents. (3) The baby John, later became the famous John the Baptist, the herald and preacher, who announced the coming of Jesus. Every baby born, and every child in class, has great possibilities for the future, within them. Reference: St. Luke. Chapter 1.

(a) Patience and Bread-fruit   *Week 9   Patience*

Our story today is an exciting tale about the value of having patience. It begins with the sailing ship, "Bounty" in the years before 1788. That is more than two hundred years ago. The Captain of the Bounty was Captain Bligh. His ship was a wooden sailing vessel, which sailed from England to the Caribbean Sea, and to the beautiful islands of the West Indies. The Ship's Mate was Fletcher Christian.

Captain Bligh was a very strict captain. This means that he required that every member of the ship's crew had to obey his orders. Captain Bligh was also an expert seaman. He knew about maps and navigation. He could guide his ship on the correct course homewards by reading the stars at night, or by finding the position of the sun at certain times of the day. He understood the direction the winds blew. The ship's crew could depend upon it, their captain was an expert sailor.

However, often he dealt harshly with his crew. His ship carried many goods to the West Indian islands, and he brought back to England, various goods in exchange. On one journey the ship was carrying pot plants as a cargo. There were gardeners from England on board the ship. These gardeners collected rare plants from the islands. They cut shoots of the trees and bushes, and transplanted them into flower pots.

As the ship was sailing on the high seas, there was a shortage of drinking water. Captain Bligh gave out strict orders that each member of the crew had only to have a small ration of water each day. Yet he also gave orders that the plants in flower pots in the cargo-hold were to be watered. No plant must die through lack of water on the way home to England. When the crew were thirsty in the hot weather, pouring water on plants seemed to be very unfair to the seamen.

Some of the plants being taken on board were from the the "Bread-fruit tree." The fruit from this tree grew to be larger than a grape-fruit, and it had a white flesh inside the skin. This is why the fruit was called, "Bread-fruit." The fruit had been used to feed local natives and slaves.

The little shoots transplanted into the flower pots arrived in England. Some were planted in Kew Gardens greenhouse, (London). They grew under glass for more than two hundred years, but never produced any Bread-fruit. Then to everyone's surprise, during the hot Summer weather of 1995, one bread-fruit grew on the tree which was now 8 metres high. It became bigger than a grape-fruit, and everyone hoped that it would grow to be as large as a foot-ball.

The patience and care for the Bread-fruit tree by the gardeners at Kew gardens for more than two hundred years had been rewarded! At long last, the Bread-fruit really had been grown in England. One national newspaper reported the joy and delight of the gardeners. The Bible tells us that one person may sow, (or transplant), and another person may water, but it is God who makes the plant grow. *Gardeners know that is worth while to be patient.*

You will want to know what happened to Captain Bligh! On another journey (1788) when the crew had been at sea for a long time, Captain Bligh had been giving punishments out to the members of the crew, who disobeyed his orders. The crew under the mate, Mr. Christian mutinied (rebelled) against the Captain. They put the Captain off the ship, into an open rowing boat, along with some loyal seamen and perhaps, gardeners. Mr Fletcher Christian became the rebel leader.

Captain Bligh was such a good seaman that he navigated the rowing boat, across the seas, guided by the stars, until he reached land. He came back to England again. The rebellious crew had to live on a far away island for the rest of their lives. They dare not return to England. I wonder whether Captain Bligh ever went to Kew Gardens to look at the Bread-fruit tree when it was very small.

Prayer:

> Lord of all Creation,
> we thank you for the fruits of the world.
> Thank you for the patience shown by gardeners.
> Grant to us all, the patience of hope.
> Bless all children, and when they are excited,
> give them patience to wait the outcome.   Amen.

Hymn:

Lord of the harvest, Lord of the field. (C&P. 2. 133)

Teachers' Note: (1) To exercise patience is difficult for all children. (2) Some things are worth waiting for in life. (Birthdays, Christmas, holidays, leaving a hospital.) (3) Kew Gardeners in God's world learn the value of patience. Two hundred years is a long time to have to wait for one tree to bear fruit. (The botanical name for Bread-fruit tree is, "artocarpus altilis.")

(b) A Pocket- Full of Patience

Week 9   Patience

Nearly all the children in the street had mountain bikes, except Bobby. His Dad had promised him a brand new bike, but then his Dad lost his job at the factory. This meant that Bobby's Dad was not earning any wages, so he could not afford the cost of buying a new bike after all. Bobby was terribly disappointed. His cousin, Emily, tried to encourage him. She was twelve years of age, and being older that Bobby, she gave him good advice. "Why do you not start to save every penny you get, and put it into a Post Office Saving Account. It will take a long time, saving that amount of money, Bobby, but you will have the satisfaction of helping to buy the bike yourself."

Bobby went away to consider what Emily had said. She being older, usually gave good advice. Bobby said to himself, "Yes, I think that I will try to save my money. Yes, I will put it into a Post Office Savings Account. What a brilliant idea! " He glanced up at his Dad, and said, "Dad, I have begun to save up for a mountain bike, how much will I need?" Dad smiled, and said, "Bobby you will need a pocket -full of patience." Bobby wondered what that meant!

His Dad gave him a one pound coin to start the savings account. His Mum gave him a little glass jar from a cupboard shelf. It was full of twenty pence coins. He counted these, and they added up to three pounds, and sixty pence. Emily whispered to him, "If you look down below the cushions on your arm-chair, and your settee, you are sure to find some money there." Bobby put his fingers through a little hole in the cloth upholstery, and found money which must have fallen out of peoples' pockets, as they sat down. He found three copper pence, and four silver ten pence coins, as well as lost pens and pencils.

Bobby put all his money, and his pocket money, into his savings account. He had seven pounds and forty-two pence already. After that, money seemed to become scarcer. Bobby remembered his Dad's words, "You will need a pocket-full of patience." He watched the other children, riding their mountain bikes, and he wished that he had the money to buy his bike. However, he had not enough after three weeks. There was no more money to be found the easy way.

After six weeks saving, Bobby found it a very long waiting time. However, he was determined to have patience. He would wait, and wait, until he had enough money. One day, Bobby thought to himself, "If I went in to the fairground and put some coins into the gaming machines, (one-armed bandits) maybe, I could win money." He tried putting one pound's worth of coins into the machines, but he lost every penny. He knew afterwards, that it was silly to do that.

The following week, his Dad came home smiling. "I've got another job at the factory." he said. His Mum smiled, because she knew that wages would be coming in to the house again. Dad spoke up. " Now, Bobby, your Mum and I will give you five pounds every week to put into your saving account at the Post Office. You can spend the little amount of pocket money you get. By the time your birthday comes, you will have enough money to buy a mountain bike."

Bobby felt his patience was running very low. He dearly wanted that mountain bike as soon as possible. Sometimes, he could feel butterflies inside his tummy, when he thought about that bike! It was difficult to have patience!

Thirty-six weeks had passed, since Bobby had begun to put £5 every week into his Post Office savings account. It was now two weeks before Bobby's birthday. Dad and Bobby went to the Post Office. They withdrew all the money from Bobby's Savings Account, which was £180.

Off Bobby and his Dad went to the bicycle shop. They chose a yellow and purple mountain bike, with black handle bars, and with eighteen speed gears. There was a lamp on the front, and a red light at the back. There was a purple bag just behind the seat, and a packet of bicycle tools inside the bag. The bike really was a beauty!

Bobby and his Dad wheeled the new bike home, despite the cardboard, and plastic packing around the wheels. Bobby wanted to try out the new bike right away. Mum and Dad said, "No Bobby, you will have to wait until your birthday before you can ride it. You will still need a pocket-full of patience." Bobby could hardly wait. Emily happened to visit Bobby, and she could see that he was very excited. Emily said, "Bobby a good way to have patience, is to take a pencil each morning, and cross off the date on the calender. It has to be one day at a time."

By the time Bobby came to June 21st. his patience was almost gone. On the 22nd. June he awoke early, and there, at last, the new mountain bike was beside his bed, unpacked and ready to go. Bobby said a little thank you prayer. "Thank you God for helping me to have a pocket full of patience, and thank you for my new mountain bike. Amen! "

Prayer:

> Lord it is very difficult to have patience.
> Forgive us if we are impatient.
> Sometimes, we find it hard to wait,
> and time seems to drag.
> Bless especially hungry, or poor children.
> In you mercy, make sick children well again.   Amen.

Hymn:

> When I needed a neighbour, where you there? (C&P. 1. 65), or (J.P. 275)

Teachers' Note: (1) Patience is testing ourselves to wait for what we want. Bobby wanted a mountain bike like the other children in the street. (2) Bobby had to try to save money himself. (Money we find may belong to someone else.) (3) Our patience may be rewarded after a long time. Faith and prayer help us to be patient.

(c) Farmer Job   *Week 9   Patience*

Farmer Job lived in the land of Uz. He was a good man, and he loved God. He had three friends, who sometimes visited him to have a good talk together. Farmer Job tried to keep away from any kind of evil. He tried to do all the good he could.

Farmer Job was wealthy. He had a family of seven sons, and three daughters. He owned 7,000 sheep, 3,000 camels, 500 teams of oxen, and 500 female donkeys. He had many servants to help him on the farm. When each one of his sons had a birthday, they invited all the other members of the family to a party. Job tried to attend all the birthday parties, one after another. Early in the morning, he always prayed for his family because one of his sons or daughters might have sinned against God.

In Heaven one day, the angels came before God. Satan, the Accuser, also came. God asked Satan where he had been. Satan answered, that he had been travelling here and there across the earth. God said to Satan, "Have you met my servant Job. He is a good man, and he does not do wrong."

Satan scoffed at God, and said, "It pays Job to love the Lord. You protect him, and his family, and property. He is a rich man, but if you took away his wealth, he would turn against you, and curse you." The Lord gave Satan permission to take away Job's riches, but ordered that he must not harm Job.

Satan went away, and began his evil work, to try and upset Farmer Job. One day, the family were dining at the oldest brother's house, when a messenger came running up with bad news. He said, "A gang of Sabbean robbers has stolen your oxen, and your donkeys, and has killed all your herdsmen, except me. I alone have escaped to tell you."

Another messenger ran up to tell Job more bad news. He said, "Lightening struck in a storm, and killed all your sheep, and the shepherds are dead. I alone have escaped to tell you."

Before he had finished talking, yet another messenger ran up to say to Job, "A gang of Chaldean rustlers have stolen all your camels, and killed their keepers. I alone have escaped to tell you."

Yet, another man came running up to the house, to tell farmer Job, that his sons and daughters has been having a feast, when a mighty wind blew down the house. The roof fell in, and all his family had been killed. He said, "I alone have escaped to tell you". Farmer Job said, "I was born with nothing, and I shall own nothing when I die. The Lord gave me everything I own, and he can choose to take everything away from me. Blessed be the name of the Lord." Job did not complain about anything which had happened.

Satan stood once more before God. The Lord said to him, "Now you have seen how my servant, Farmer Job has behaved well. He is really the finest man in the whole world." Satan answered. "If you harm his health, then you will find out, that Job will turn against you." God allowed Satan to attack Job and his body came out in boils.

Job's wife was no help to him in his illness. She said to her husband, "Why are you still trying to be a godly man, when God has allowed all this to happen to you. Why do you not just curse God", Job answered his wife. "You are talking like a heathen woman. God may send pleasant or unpleasant things upon us, just as he sees best." In all these sad happenings, Job never once spoke against God.

Farmer Job's three friends visited him, but they saw that he was very ill. After seven days they came back again. Job said to them, "I feel so ill now, that I wish I had never been born." His three friends began to argue that Job must have done something wrong in the past. Job knew he had not done any wrong.

God was proud of Farmer Job because of his patient faith. Later, God blessed Job, and restored to him all his wealth and his property. He became an even richer farmer than before. When Farmer Job became rich again, he still loved God in the same way, as when he had lost everything.

Prayer:

> Lord our Father, forgive us,
> that sometimes we are impatient.
> We thank you for Job's patience.
> Grant that we, young and older people,

may have strong faith in God,
and patience that endures all things.   Amen.

Hymn:

Peace perfect peace is the gift of Christ our Lord. (C&P. 1. 53)

Teachers' Note: (1) Patience is made up of a quiet faith in God, and a strong will, never to doubt the goodness of God. Children also may learn to be patient. (2) Job passed through real disasters in his life. All God's people may have to face difficulties. (3) God never forsook Farmer Job. God remained Job's unseen friend. At the end of the testing, Job was restored to his farm and possessions. He raised another family. His health returned to him. In all this, Job kept his faith. Reference. Job Chapter 1, verses 6-21.

(a) The Reason, "Why." *Week 10   Motives*

It is very important to know the reason why anyone acts as they do. At school, when Marion Tyler fell down the stairs, the Headteacher had to find out why Marion fell. Was her eyesight so poor, that she missed one of the steps? Or was it that she had a dizzy feeling in her head that made her fall? Or was it that some rough pupil behind her, had given her a push? Or did she trip over something? It is important to ask, "Why" things happen.

The following story, has a problem in it, which everyone in the Assembly can think about, and decide whether the Red Indian Chief was a wise Chief or not.

Two red Indian men who lived in Western Canada were very good friends. They often went out together on their reservation to hunt wild animals as their food. One Indian was named Running Deer because he could run through the forest very quickly. The other Indian was was named Shining Star, because he could never be lost in the forest. He could guide himself home, by looking at the stars, or seeing where the grass had been trodden down.

Both Indians had hunting rifles, and they were hunting rabbits, or any small game, such as wild duck. They were very brave men, and unafraid of wild animals. As they made their way through the dense forest, a large grizzly bear unexpectedly attacked them. Running Deer escaped by running through bushes, but the grizzly bear caught Shining Star in his strong furry arms. A grizzly bear can crush a man to death, just by squeezing him tightly.

Running Deer seeing his friend being crushed by the grizzly Bear, raised his rifle, and quickly fired a shot to kill the bear. However, the bear happened to turn, and the shot went into his Indian friend's shoulder instead. Running Deer fired a second shot, and killed the bear, and saved the life of his friend. Now, Running

Deer had to carry the wounded Shining Star home on his shoulder to his log cabin.

Shining Star had a squaw, (Indian wife) and she was very angry, when she found out that her husband had been shot by Running Deer. She thought that Running Deer had been careless. She went to the Indian Chief, at the Indian Court, and asked him to condemn Running Deer for shooting her husband.

The Indian Chief considered the matter carefully. The first question he asked Running Deer was, "Why did you shoot your best friend?" Running Deer answered, "My honoured Chief, I fired the first shot in order to save my Friend's life, but the grizzly bear moved as I pulled the trigger, so I happened to shoot my Friend in the shoulder instead. I killed the dangerous bear with the second shot."

The wise and honoured Chief, pronounced his verdict. He said, "If Running Deer had simply shot Shining Star in the shoulder, then that would have been very wrong. It would have been a crime. However, the reason why, Running Deer shot his friend, was that he was trying to save him from being crushed by the grizzly bear. *HIS INTENTIONS WERE OF THE VERY BEST KIND*. It was an accident! Running Deer is a brave man, and worthy of thanks for saving his Friend's life."

Shining Star's wife accepted the Chief's ruling on the case. Soon, Shining Star was well again, and he once more went out with his friend to to hunt rabbits for their dinner pot. They were glad that their Chief had asked the question, WHY? the accident had happened. WHY? tells us about INTENTIONS (reason why) . It is a very important word, if we are to make judgements on other people.

Prayer:

> Lord, you know our deepest thoughts.
> You know our intentions.
> Give us all pure hearts,
> that we may never knowingly cause harm
> to anyone.
> Forgive us if we have judged anyone wrongly.   Amen.

Hymn:

> Make me a channel of your peace. (C&P. 2. 147) or (J.P. 161)

Teachers' Note: (1) This story is meant to be a children's introduction to the idea of "intention." "WHY" is an important word. "ACCIDENT" is an important concept in the child's world. (2) One of the Indian friends hurt the other one. Children may hurt each other. (3) Forgiveness and understanding come from the teaching of Jesus. (Forgive seventy times seven).

(b) The Green Dress

Helen's Mum used to be a Dancer on the stage, before she was married. In a big trunk upstairs, she kept one of her beautiful dresses from her dancing days. Sometimes she would put the magnificent sparkling green dress against herself, and look into a long mirror. Mum imagined herself again on the stage, and in her mind, she could see the hundreds of people in the audience, who sat and watched her perform in those days. She remembered how she sang and danced, and how the people clapped their hands, when she had finished her act. Helen knew that her Mum really loved that dress, more than any other garment she possessed.

Helen used to examine the green fabric, and the hundreds of little sequins which had been sewn on to the dress sparkled under the lights. There were beautiful pearls, and coloured glass butterflies sewn around the top of the dress. It was a dress fit for a queen to wear. It must have been very expensive to make. Helen's Mum used to put the dress away into the big trunk with such care. Helen thought that the green dress must have been the most important thing in her life.

Time passed by, and Helen was now eleven years old. She was in year six at the school. She would soon leave the Primary school, to attend the comprehensive school, about a mile up the road. Helen's school decided to hold a "Leaving Party, and Disco" for all the older pupils of thc Top Class. It was to be a real party, where the boys and girls were told to wear their smartest clothes.

Now Helen's Dad had been unemployed, like so many more. Helen knew that her Mum could not afford to buy her a new dress, until her Dad was working again. However, Helen was a sensible girl, and decided that she would wear the spotted red dress she had when she was on holiday the year before. Helen had grown taller, as all girls do at her age. She thought, "Maybe, Mum will let down the hem, and then it will fit me."

Helen told her Mum about the "End of Year Party and Disco" for the leavers in the top class." Helen said, I haven't got a new dress, but last year's red spotted one will have to do instead." Mum looked very thoughtful. Next day, when Helen came home from school, she was amazed to find that her Mum had cut her beautiful green dress into four large pieces. She took a measuring tape, and measured Helen around the waist; then she measured her from her neck to her hemline. Then she measured the breadth of her shoulders.

Two days afterwards, when Helen came home from school, the most beautiful dress she had ever seen, was waiting for her to wear. It was a perfectly new dress, made from the fabric of her mum's dress. Butterflies and little pearls were sewn on it here and there. It fitted Helen perfectly. When the evening of the Leavers Party and Disco came around, Helen looked beautiful. Her dress was more dazzling that any other girl's dress. Everyone was commenting on how well she looked. Many asked her privately what shop she had bought it from, and how much it had cost! Helen knew how to keep a secret. Even the boys smiled at her.

It was a terrific Party and Disco, and Helen was excited, and very tired, when she came home that night. She jumped into her bed. Her Mum came up to say "Good Night." Helen looked at her Mum, and said, "Mum, I want to know why you cut up your most beautiful dress?" Her Mum smiled and answered, "Helen, when you really love anyone, you will make any sacrifice for that person. I loved you, a thousand times more than I loved that dress."

Helen gave her Mum a "Good-night kiss", and went fast asleep. She felt that she was the happiest girl in all the world. She had found out "WHY" her Mum had cut up her finest dress.

To love someone, and be loved, is the most beautiful feeling in all the world. "Love give, and gives, and gives again." Helen remembered the words which she had heard in church. "Love bears all things, believes all things, hopes all things, endures all things. Love never fails. So these three remain, faith , hope and love, but the greatest of these is LOVE.

Prayer:

> Lord, our Father, teach us that love has its own reasons.
> We thank you for your great love for us,
> in sending Jesus to be our Saviour.
> May parents love children,
> and children love their parents.
> and may we all love each other.   Amen.

Hymn:

> Love will never come to an end. (C&P. 2. 99)

Teachers' Note: (1). Helen was astonished that her Mum should cut up her fine dress on her behalf. (2) However, love always tries to give the best. (3) God loves every person. Jesus taught his disciples "to love one another" The love of parents for their family is what keeps a family together.

(c) Good Intentions

Week 10   Motives

The First Story

Matthew was a Tax Collector. The Roman soldiers had conquered the country. This meant that Judea and Galilee became part of the Roman empire. The Roman government made the Jewish people pay money as taxes. The money the people paid was used to pay for the expenses of the Roman government. No one liked paying taxes, and no-one liked any of their own people to became Tax-collectors.

No-one would like Matthew, because he collected money from the Jews to give it to the Romans.

Tax-collectors often charged their own people higher taxes than they should have done, and they kept the extra money for themselves. One day, Jesus happened to see Matthew sitting at his table. Jesus said to Matthew, "Follow me." Matthew from that moment became one of Jesus disciples.

Matthew made a fine meal at his home. He invited Jesus to come and eat with him. Jesus accepted the invitation. The religious people who knew Matthew's past life, felt that he was real a bad person. "Just imagine mixing with tax-collectors," they said. However, Jesus loved to help bad people to change their ways.

Jesus said to the faultfinders who accused him, "You are to think of me as you would think of a Doctor. I have come to help people who are ill, not those who are well. I am here to help these people to believe in God." Jesus always had good intentions.

The Second Story

Here is another story to illustrate the importance of good intentions. Farmer Haywood looked over his hedge and he saw the Patterson twins in his orchard. The Patterson twins were a boy and a girl aged ten years old. Farmer Haywood thought to himself, "Those twins are stealing my best eating apples." He 'phoned the police and told them that he had two thieves in his orchard stealing apples.

He had crouched watching behind the hedge. Then, he rushed out. He caught the Patterson twins, "How dare you steal my apples," he said. Just at that moment, a police car arrived, with two police officers inside. One was a Policeman, and the other was a Lady Police Officer. Farmer Haywood handed the Patterson twins over to the police.

The Lady Police Officer, said to Farmer Haywood. "Now we are not arresting anyone at the moment. Let the twins speak for themselves." She asked, "Why were you twins in the orchard?" Both twins smiled, and one said, "Holly, our cat is up the tree. We have come to coax her down." The two police officers looked, and sure enough, there was Holly, the cat, sitting on a high branch of the tree.

Farmer Haywood realised that he had been wrong in accusing the twins. They had utterly no intention of stealing the farmer's apples. He said that he was very sorry. The Police Officers asked the twins if they wanted to take the case any further. The twins were kind-hearted children. They said, "No we will forgive Farmer Haywood for making false accusations against us. We think that he did not really intend to harm us."

So the twins, Farmer Haywood, and the two Police Officers went away, saying to each other, "Yes! Intentions are very important." Meanwhile, Holly the cat, came down the tree, and followed the twins back home. The twins gave Holly a cuddle, and afterwards, they gave her a saucer of milk.

Prayer:

>Heavenly Father, look at our intentions.
>In school, help us to try to do better.
>Forgive us if we have unkind intentions.
>Help us to think well of other people.
>Bless all children, keep us kind-hearted.   Amen.

Hymn:

>Thank you, Lord, for every new day. (C&P. 1. 32)

Teachers' Note: (1) Jesus mixed with people such as Matthew who were known as "sinners." He became their friends in order to help them become better people. Matthew later became a writer, and wrote a source book of the sayings of Jesus. It later became known as "Gospel of St. Matthew." (2) Farmer Haywood falsely accused the twins, before he heard their story. (3) Intentions are hidden inside us. We may have bad intentions, or good intentions. Some happenings are accidental, and not intended to happen.

(a) The Lost Name-Tag   *Week 11   Disobedience*

It was a beautiful Summer's day. The children at the Infant school were being taken by coach to the seaside, for a day's outing by the sea. Every girl and boy had a name-tag tied, or pinned to their clothing. If children became lost, their names, and the address of the school could be clearly read on the name-tag. Soon everyone was seated in the special coach, and they moved off. The Teacher counted the children, and wrote 52 in her notebook.

Some of the children were playing with their name tags, and even taking them off. The Teacher had to stand up in the coach, and tell everyone not to remove their name-tags. The children sang songs and chatted on the journey.

Lawrence in the Top Class, sometimes was disobedient. He had been playing with his name-tag, when he was singing with the other children. He had taken it off, and now completely had forgotten all about it. The name-tag fell off his lap, and dropped below the coach seat. No-one noticed that Lawrence had lost it.

When they reached Blackpool, the children left the coach in an orderly queue to go to the Pleasure Beach with three of the teachers. The Teachers again counted the number of children getting out. They numbered 52. The children and Teachers spent two hours at the Pleasure Beach, before getting back into the coach, to go to a specially reserved room to have their lunch. They were watching the famous Blackpool tramcars travelling along the iron tram rail beside the sea. Soon they were back in the room, and the children were enjoying their sandwiches and pop.

The Teachers again counted the children, and this time they only numbered 51. Someone was missing! It turned out that Lawrence was the missing person. They looked around the room, in the toilets, and outside the front door, but Lawrence could not be found. The Teachers immediately, telephoned for the Police, and gave them a good description of Lawrence. They said to the Police Sergeant, "You will know that it is Lawrence, when you find him, because he is wearing a name-tag pinned to his jacket."

No-one thought much more about it, until everyone climbed into the coach to go to the Zoo, and one of the girls found Lawrence's name-tag lying on the floor, beneath the seat. The Teachers and children were really worried now. Lawrence had lost his name and the address of the school. His disobedience was spoiling the children's outing, and worrying the Teachers, and also taking up Police time, searching for him.

Meanwhile, Lawrence was watching the people riding on the roller-coaster, and others driving the dodgems. Suddenly he realised that he was alone, in a very large crowd of people. He was terrified! His Mum had warned him to keep with the other children.

Lawrence walked up to an Attendant, and told him that he was lost. The Attendant took out a pocket telephone, and telephoned the police. In a short time the police car had arrived, and Lawrence felt safe again.

The only problem now was that the children and Teachers had to be back home at their school for 3-30p.m. The coach had to set off, without Lawrence. Everyone in the coach was feeling sad, about losing Lawrence. About ten miles along the road, a police car came up at speed behind the coach, and flashed its headlights.

The coach stopped, and the Policeman came out of his car, holding Lawrence by the hand. Lawrence felt ashamed that he had caused so much trouble for everyone on the school outing. Lawrence climbed into the coach. The policemen smiled, and said, "Good bye." One of the girls gave the lost name-tag back to Lawrence. He pinned it on his jacket. He promised his Teacher that he would never be disobedient again. Soon, they were back home at the school again. Lawrence's Mum heard what had happened. At first, she was very cross with her son, but after a while she forgave him. She said to Lawrence, "All is well that ends well!"

Prayer:

We thank you, our heavenly Father,
for our Teachers and Leaders.
Help us to be obedient at school,
when we are in our teachers' care.
Teach us to care for each other.
We pray for sick children,
make them well again.   Amen.

Hymn:

There are hundreds of sparrows, thousands, millions. (C&P. 1. 15).

Teachers' Note: (1) School rules are always for our own good. (2) Some children may be disobedient, and cause trouble for their Teachers and school friends. (3) Disobedience brings its own punishments on wrong-doing. Lawrence had a very unhappy day at Blackpool. Yet, the happy fact is that he had learnt his lesson.

(b) The Genesis Stories   *Week 11   Disobedience*

(If this Assembly is rather long for the occasion, the Leader may prefer to read from the paragraph beginning, "On the sixth day.")

First part

The Bible tells us how the Hebrew and Christian people were taught about the beginning of the world, before the age of science. There are several parable-stories, full of meaning and deep truths about the friendship of God with his people.

On the first day, God created the skies and the earth. On this first day, the earth was without form or shape, and water was everywhere. Darkness was over the waters. The Spirit of God moved over the waters. God said, "Let there be light, and there was light." The light , he called "day" The darkness, "God called, "night."

The first day, was not morning and evening, but rather, evening and morning!

On the second day, God divided the waters, so that there was water above the clouds, and then there were the skies, and water below the skies. (This was the old world view that the earth was like a saucer, with water both down and up in the sky.)

On the third day, God divided the land from the water. The dry land, God called "earth". and the water, he called "sea." The earth began to grow green grass, plants, and trees bearing fruit. God saw it all and thought how good it looked.

On the fourth day, God said, "Let there be lights in the sky, to divide day and night." The Sun was made to rule the day, and the Moon was made to shine by night. God also made the stars to shine in the sky. Again, God thought it looked good.

On the fifth day, God made all the fish in the seas. He also made all the birds. He looked at his handiwork, and God thought that it was good.

On the sixth day, God made all the animals, and all the reptiles, and creeping things. *Then he made Adam, the first man,* from the dust of the ground. He breathed into Adam, and Adam became a living person. He caused Adam to fall into a deep sleep.

God took flesh and bone, from Adam's side, and he made a woman, who became a wife for Adam. God named the woman, "Eve." God now gave authority to Adam and Eve to have power over all the fish, birds and animals. God looked at his handiwork, and said, "This is good."

On the seventh day, God rested from all his work. A damp mist covered the earth, and watered the whole earth.

Now, God had put Adam and Eve in a beautiful garden, which he called the "Garden of Eden." He told Adam that he could eat any of the fruits on the trees in the garden, except one. This exception, was a very special tree, in the middle of the garden, sometimes called "the tree of the knowledge of good and evil," or the, "Tree of life.' On this special tree grew the forbidden fruit. "If you eat this fruit, you will die," said God.

The Second Part

Now both Adam and Eve were naked, because they had never worn any clothing. There was a Serpent in the garden, which could talk. It had evil intentions. The Serpent told the woman, Eve, that she could eat of the tree of life. Eve believed the Serpent. She took some of the forbidden fruit, and shared it with her husband, Adam. Immediately, after they had eaten the fruit from the tree, they both realised that they were naked. They made clothes from fig leaves sewn together.

God came to walk in the garden of Eden, when it was cool in the evening. God called out, "Adam , where are you?" Adam answered, "Because I was naked, I hid myself." God asked him, "How did you know that you were naked? Have you eaten the forbidden fruit, Adam?"

Then, Adam put the blame on Eve. He said, "This woman, Eve, gave me the fruit, and I ate it." Eve in turn, tried to put the blame on the serpent. She said, "The Serpent tempted me, and I ate the forbidden fruit." God said, to the Serpent, "Because you have tempted Adam and Eve, you shall crawl on your belly, and eat the dust, all your life. People will kill snakes in days to come."

God made clothing from skins for Adam and Eve. Because they had been disobedient, God drove both Adam and Eve out of the garden. He placed an angel with a flaming sword, on the East side of the Garden of Eden, to prevent anyone ever again eating of the tree of life.

Adam became a farmer, and he had to dig the ground. Weeds began to grow in the fields. Later, they had two sons, whom they named Cain and Abel. Cain became a gardener, while Abel became a shepherd. One day they had a quarrel and Cain killed his brother, Abel. Years passed by, and finally the family eventually died, just as God had warned them.

The point of this story is that because Adam and Eve were disobedient, everything went wrong. They were never allowed back into the beautiful garden. Disobedience to God's laws usually brings trouble on disobedient people.

Prayer:

Father God, we thank you for the stories
which we read in the Bible.
Show us how to read, and understand them.
We thank you for your love for all people.
If we have been disobedient, forgive us.
Teach us to choose good rather than evil.   Amen.

Hymn:

He's got the whole world in his hands. (C&P. 1. 19) or (C.P. 78).

Teachers' Note: (1) Children in a T.V. age are gradually becoming aware of the difference between history, and parable-stories. Parable stories contain deep truths, and early answers to questions. (Who made the world? Who was the first man? Who was the first woman? Why is there sin in the world? Why has a snake no legs. Why are babies born? Why can we not see God? Why do weeds grow?) Parable-stories are not fairy tales, but rather teaching stories. (2) The story about the Tree illustrates our ability to choose between good or evil. (3) It is important to note that, God still loves his people, even when they sin against him.

(c) The Golden Calf   *Week 11   Disobedience*

Moses was the Leader of the Hebrews. He had led the Hebrews out of Egypt, where they had been slaves. He had led them through the Red sea on dry land. Now the large multitude of people were walking through the desert towards the Promised land. Moses was a good Leader, because he taught the Hebrews to serve the Lord as their God. He taught the people to worship only one God, who was the Lord.

Moses had gone up a mountain in order to be alone with God. He wanted God to give Commandments to him, so that the Hebrew people would know how to behave. Moses remained up the mountain for quite a long time. There was a cloud around the mountain, so the people did not see what was happening to Moses. This cloud was the presence of the glory of God. Moses received the Ten Commandments from God written on two tablets of stone.

The Hebrew people were very anxious that Moses, their Leader, had been away for such a long time. They thought that, maybe, he would not be coming back. The people gathered around Aaron, the brother of Moses. They told Aaron how they felt without their Leader. Aaron, told the people to collect all the gold ear rings from the ears of their wives, sons, and daughters. There were thousands of people wearing gold ornaments.

Aaron melted all the gold down, by using the heat of a fire. He used his tools to make a Golden Calf. He set the Golden Calf on a rock, and called the people together. "This shall be your god, O Hebrew People," he shouted to them. Next day, Aaron arranged to hold a Feast day. The people worshipped the Golden Calf as though it were really a god. They made offerings unto it. Then they sang and danced before the Golden Calf.

Now God was still holding his conversation with Moses up on the mountain. God said to Moses, "Those Hebrew people of mine have forgotten the true God already. They are singing and dancing, and worshipping a Golden calf." God said to Moses, "I am very displeased with my people, for worshipping a false god." Moses pleaded with God to forgive the people.

When Moses came down the mountain, he brought the two tablets of stone in his hands. On the tablets of stone were written the Ten Commandments for the people. When Moses arrived back in the camp among the people, they were singing, and dancing before the Golden Calf. Moses became very angry, because they had forgotten the true God. He took the two tablets of stone, and threw them down on the ground, where they broke into pieces. Then, he took the Golden Calf and also broke it into pieces.

Moses again, prayed that God would forgive the people for worshipping the Golden Calf, instead of the Lord. God was good, and he did forgive them for their sin. Moses went into the Tent of the Lord, which was a special worship tent outside the camp. When Moses was inside the Tent speaking with God, the cloud that had been around the mountain, moved down to the door of the Tent. When the people saw the cloud in front of the door of the Tent of the Lord, they knew that God was again speaking with Moses in private.

Prayer:

Teach us Lord, to worship you,
With all our heart, and with all our mind.

Help us to remember that although
God is unseen, that he is our best friend.
Bless our School, and help us all
to keep the rules, which are for our good.   Amen.

Hymn:

Praise the Lord in the rhythm of your music. (C&P. 1. 33).

Teachers' Note: (1) Teachers sometime must be absent. That is the time for children to be loyal and true. (2) Aaron set the people a bad example, by making a Golden Calf for worship. He was a poor Leader. (3) Moses was the good Leader who was very close to God. He loved the people very much. Yet, he had a hot temper. Reference Exodus Ch. 32.

(a) The Tenderfoot   *Week 12   End of School Year*

Swift Eagle was a Red Indian boy who lived among the Rocky Mountains in Canada. His parents had given the baby the name of Swift Eagle, because they believed that he would grow up to become an Indian Brave, who would be a strong member of their tribe. Swift Eagle was just like any other boy of his age. He had to attend the school on the reservation, where the Indians lived.

The reservation covered a vast area, of the Western Rocky Mountains. The area had large forests which grew on the side of the mountains. There were many beautiful streams, and lakes. Wild animals, such as reindeer, bears and wolves lived in the forests. Lumberjacks cut down hundreds of trees each day, for the paper mill. Many of the Indians were also expert lumberjacks.

Swift Eagle's family now lived in a log cabin, and no longer lived in a wigwam. His father, Running Deer, was also a very skillful hunter. When his son, became twelve years of age, he would become a fully recognised Brave, but only after he had gone through the Test. It seemed a long time until Swift Eagle, reached his twelfth birthday.

The father told his son about the Test. When evening came, he would have to go into the forest, all alone. He would be expected to walk through the forest during the long dark hours of the night, until the sun shone next morning. At night many of the wild animals prowled around in the darkness. If an Indian boy had enough courage to remain all night in the forest, this would prove to every other Indian, that Swift Eagle was ready to become an Indian Brave, and to be a fully fledged member of the Tribe.

That evening, as the moon shone down, Swift Eagle was taken by his father to the edge of the forest. The boy carried his bow and arrows, a hunting knife, and his tomahawk (an axe). He was not allowed to take his father's hunting rifle with him. The boy bid his father, "Good Night." Running Deer walked away into the cover of the darkness.

Now the boy, was alone, his heart began to beat fiercely. At first, he could see nothing, but as his eyes became used to the darkness, he could see the tall Douglas Fir trees, the mighty Redwood Trees, and thousands of Pine Trees. growing high into the black sky. He had never been alone in the dark forest before. He heard the little animals, such as rabbits, badgers, foxes, and otters moving about the banks of the rivers. He could see the moon and the stars shining through the trees. He found his direction, when he took note of the position of the Evening Star (Venus) and the North Star.

The mountain forest was a strange place at night. All sorts of moths and insects were flying about. He could hear one wolf howling miles away, and another she-wolf was howling back her answer. The Indian boy, Swift Eagle, believed in God, although he called God by the name of, "The Great Spirit." The boy made his journey along the forest path in the darkness. He knew that the Great Spirit would help him through. He was not afraid, because he had been used to the forest during the daytime.

It was a long night, but Swift Eagle, continued his journey. It is a very beautiful sight to see the moon shining through the trees. The boy was moved inwardly by the beauty of forest. Then, his feelings changed. He felt it an eerie place to be alone. He felt as if many animal eyes were watching his every move in the darkness. As he stumbled occasionally, or as he stepped aside to let a snake glide past, he was conscious that someone was watching him. It was a strange feeling of which he could not rid himself. Yet he encouraged himself, that no-one could be there to harm him. He prayed to the Great Spirit for strength. Yet there definitely was SOMETHING there! He felt it in his bones. He clutched his bow and arrow.

At long last, the streaks of light appeared in the morning sky. Then the sun arose again, and it became day. What the boy never knew was that he had been safe all the time. A shadowy figure of an Indian chief had been following him all through the night. The dark figure had been carrying a hunting rifle in order to protect the boy. All through the dark night, his protector had been hiding behind the trees. He had been treading softly just like an animal, rather than a human being.

In the glory of the morning sunshine, the boy looked behind him. He suddenly saw the figure come out of the forest. It was his own father carrying a hunting rifle. Running Deer put his arms around his son. He said, "You have completed the Test, Swift Eagle! You are now a fully fledged Indian Brave. I am proud of you, my son."

The Indian boy was glad to see his father after the experience of a long night in the forest. Then, at once, he realised that he had never really been left by himself. His father had been the dark figure who had been hiding behind the trees, and following him. His Father had been guarding him all the night through with his hunting rifle. The Father and son walked home together to their log cabin, for a breakfast of freshly cooked salmon. Swift Eagle held his head high. He was no longer a Tenderfoot. He had passed the Test. He was now a real honourable Indian Brave.

Children can learn two lessons from this story. First, we all have to pass through Tests in this life. It will not be, that they must walk though a Canadian mountain forest at night. Yet, there are other Tests we must face, such as leaving the Primary School, and going to the secondary school. That may be a difficult test for us.

The second lesson is that God is our Heavenly Father. We must never forget, that although we cannot see him with our eyes, God is always there, whether it is dark or light. The twenty third Psalm says, "Though I walk through the valley of the shadow of death, you are with me." Our Father, God, is with us, helping us through every Test in our lives.

Prayer:

Heavenly Father, help us when we feel afraid.
Teach us not to be fearful of the tests of life,
knowing that your presence is always with us.
Keep us from worrying, and grant us faith.
Make us to be strong in the Lord.
Bless all children going through some Test.   Amen.

Hymn:

Lord of all hopefulness. (C&P. 1. 52) or (J. P. 157)

Teachers' Note: (1) Everyone passes through some Test. eg. Doing exams, going to the dentist, being in the dark, going to the secondary school, illness, or learning to swim. (2) The end of the school year can be a journey into the unknown for many children, because they do not know what lies ahead. (3) The Indian boy, found out later that he was not alone in the dark forest. His father was protecting him all the time. Although, we cannot see God, he is always taking care of us. Note, that the Indian boy was very careful.

(b) The Two Davids   *Week 12   End of School Year*

Here is a story about being yourself. The children attended a school which was situated in a lovely green Welsh valley. In "class three", there was a small boy named David Evans. To the other children, he was known as "little David." In "class four," there was a big boy, also named David Evans. To the other children, he was known as "big David."

Of course, big David was one year older than little David. They knew each other very well, and both boys played with the other children. No one ever bothered that they both shared the same name, because "Evans" is a well known name in Wales.

It was the end of the Summer term, which is also the end of the school year. The Teachers were working very hard, preparing a report for every girl and boy in each of the different classes. When the teachers had completed writing the reports, they were put on the Headteacher's desk for her to sign. There they lay in two separate piles, Class three, and Class four.

The caretaker, came into the room when it was empty, to answer the telephone which had been ringing for a long time. As he lifted the receiver, he accidently knocked over the two piles of school reports, which fell on the floor. He picked them up from behind the Headteacher's desk, and put them into two piles again. He did not realise that he had mixed up two of the School Reports.

Next day the children took their reports home in envelopes to their parents. Big David's parents read his report. The Sport's teacher wrote, that David was small for his age, and that he did not like football. (David was tallest in class four, and he loved football.) The English report said that David was very good at English, but his writing was careless. (David really preferred to watch television much more than he liked to read, but he was a beautiful writer).

At the end of the report, it read that since David was such a good reader, that he would be awarded, "the school prize for being the Best Reader of the Year." Big David's parents were delighted to read about their son gaining the school Reading Prize, but they did not like any other part of the report.

Little David's parents also received a report. It reported that David was a tall lad for his age. (David was the smallest in class three). David was amazed, when the report said that he loved football, while he knew in himself that he hated it. His mother was angry, when the report said that David was a very poor reader, and never used the school library. (David loved books).

However, at the bottom of the page, little David's parents were very pleased to read that David had been been awarded the School silver cup for Best Sports-Person of the Year. They did not like any other part of the report. Big David's parents, and little David's parents said to their sons, what parents always say to their children. "We knew that you could do better, but we are delighted that you won the Class prize." Both boys just scratched their heads, not knowing what to say, because they knew themselves better than anyone else.

At the Annual School Leaving Day, the parents all arrived at the school hall. The Head Teacher said that she was delighted to see so many parents present. The children all sat in rows, dressed in their best clothes. After the children sang as a Choir, the Headteacher presented the prizes to children who had done especially well that year.

All at once, she stopped reading her speech. She said, "Ladies and gentlemen, I am afraid that there has been a dreadful mistake, in giving out the reports. It is a case of, "the first shall be last, and the last shall be first". She continued her prepared speech. "Big David Evans will not receive the, Best Reader of the Year prize, after all, that will go to little David Evans" Everyone clapped heartily, as little David Evans came forward to receive his Best Reader prize. He was proud of himself, because he loved books.

The Headteacher read on, "I am afraid that little David Evans will not receive the silver cup for the Best Sports-person of the Year. That prize will go to big David Evans." Again, everyone applauded. Big David was proud of himself, because he really loved sport.

All the children were especially happy, because the matter had been sorted out fairly. School reports are very useful, because they tell us the truth about ourselves. Both big David and little David exchanged their school reports, and they both went home, holding their prizes. Both boys were glad that they were named "David Evans." Nevertheless, they preferred to be themselves.

Prayer:

> Heavenly Father, we are your family.
> We are all your children.
> Lord, you have made each of us different persons.
> Yet you love us all, for what we are.
> Teach us to use our gifts and talents
> so that at then end of next year,
> we may be better people,
> and stronger in our faith.   Amen.

Hymn:

> The ink is black, the page is white. (C&P. 1. 67)

Teachers' Note: (1). Both boys liked different subjects in school. Big David clearly was good at sport, and little David liked books. However, tall children can also like books, and smaller children may love sport. (2) School reports are very necessary in order to find out what progress children are making. Later on, children will develop new talents. (3) Children know themselves, and feel more comfortable in some subjects, rather than in others. The two Davids were good friends.

(c) The Three Questions   *Week 12   The End of the School Year*

At the end of the Summer Term, schools usually have Tests. These Tests are usually in the form of questions. We are expected to answer the questions. Sometimes we write the answers. Sometimes we use our voices to say the answer. Sometimes we work with our hands, to provide the answer. (Art, or cookery) Our school reports often tell us which tests we do easily, and which tests we find more difficult. Today's story is about three questions which Jesus asked Peter.

It all happened after Jesus had risen from the grave. For a time the disciples did not always know exactly where Jesus was. He seemed to appear in their presence, and then to disappear again. The disciples said, "We are going fishing." Peter also went along with the other disciples. They launched their fishing boat, and sailed out into the sea. They let down their nets, and fished all night through, but they did not catch any fish.

Early next morning, Jesus was standing on the shore. He saw the disciples in their fishing boat, but they did not recognise him. He called out to them, "My friends, have you caught any fish?" They shouted back, "No." Maybe, Jesus being higher up the shore, saw the sea gulls flying over a shoal of fish, as they often do around our shores. Jesus answered back, "Throw your net on the right side of the ship, and you will catch some."

The fishermen let down their nets on the right hand side of the boat, as they had been told. To their amazement, their nets were filled to overflowing, with wriggling fish. Indeed, the net was so full, that they were unable to pull in the net. As soon as John heard the voice, he said to Peter, "It is the Lord." Since the boat was near the shore, Peter, immediately, jumped out, into the shallow water. He began to pull the boat, towards the shore, while the men in the boat towed the full net of fish behind them.

On the shore, quite near them, a fire was burning brightly. There were fish being cooked, and bread being baked upon it. Jesus said, "Bring some of the fish you have caught, and we will cook them also on the fire." Peter went into the little fishing boat, and he counted 153 fish. Jesus cooked some of the fish. He gave each man a piece of fish along with a piece of bread, for his breakfast. By this time, the disciples had recognised that the stranger on the shore, was really the Lord Jesus.

Now, Simon Peter, (whose father was named John), had previously denied three times that he knew Jesus. At that time, Jesus had been arrested, and Peter had been afraid of also being arrested by the Roman soldiers.

Jesus stood near Peter. Jesus asked him, "Simon son of John, do you love me?" "Yes, Lord," Peter answered, "you know that I love you." Jesus said, "Feed my lambs." A second time Jesus asked Peter, "Simon, son of John, do you love me?"

Again, Peter answered, "Lord, you know that I love you!" Jesus said this time, "Take care of my sheep."

The third time Jesus asked, "Simon, son of John, do you love me?" Peter by this time was offended by being asked the same question for the third time. He answered, "Lord, you know all things; you know that I love you." Jesus answered, "Feed my sheep."

All at once, Peter realised that the reason why, Jesus had asked him the same question three times, was because he had denied three times that he was a disciple of Jesus. Peter from that day forward, never denied Jesus again. He never boasted about himself any more.

Some time after this had happened, Peter and John were in Jerusalem. They were walking up to the Jewish Temple. It was about three o'clock in the afternoon. A poor lame beggar man asked Peter for money. Peter said to him, "I do not have any money, but what I have, I will give you. In the name of Jesus of Nazareth, rise up and walk."

The beggar was cured. He was no longer lame. As his legs became stronger, he began to jump for joy in the street. He gave God thanks because he had been healed. This story shows us that Jesus had forgiven Peter for the three times he had denied him. It also shows us that God was pleased with Peter, and that he could heal sick people through him.

This is the last week of the School year. Children have been answering questions in class through-out the past months. If we are able, we must always try to give the best answer, and the most honest answer to a question. Even when we are on holiday, we may ask ourselves questions. What is the name of a wild flower we may have seen? How many kinds of fish can we name.? What is the name of the ship, or aeroplane, or train, in which we have travelled? What are the names of the Twelve disciples? What is the name of the best person we have ever heard about? Jesus!

Prayer:

> Heavenly Father, we thank you for St. Peter.
> We thank you for his change of life,
> from being weak and fearful person,
> to becoming a strong Leader.
> Bless all children and Teachers,
> as we separate for the holidays
> Help us to find answers to our questions. Amen.

Hymn:

> Now thank we all our God. (C&P. 1. 38) or (J.P. 175)

Teachers' Note: (1). Peter was afraid, and denied three times that he was a friend of Jesus. To jog Peter's memory, Jesus asked three questions. (2). Peter loved the Lord, and he became a dependable leader for the disciples. (3) A good way to learn is to try to answer questions honestly. In our hearts, let us give thanks to God for being able to successfully reach the end of the School Year